Dr Martin E...
biomedical t...
list of militar...
for the benefi...
Europe for the ... anniversary of the D-Day land-
ings. This led to a list of maritime museums which
he has compiled with his wife Dr Janet West, herself
an expert on maritime decorative arts, particularly
scrimshaw. She is a member of the Scott Polar
Research Institute, a fellow of Wolfson College,
Cambridge, and Advisory Curator of Scrimshaw at
the Kendall Whaling Museum in Massachusetts.

MARITIME MUSEUMS

A Guide
to the Collections
and Museum Ships
in Britain and Ireland

by
Martin H Evans & Janet West

CHATHAM PUBLISHING

LONDON

First published in Great Britain in 1998
by Chatham Publishing, 61 Frith Street, London W1V 5TA

Chatham Publishing is an imprint of Gerald Duckworth & Co Ltd

British Library Cataloguing in Publication Data
A catalogue record for this book is available from the British Library

ISBN 1 86176 077 9

Designed and typeset by Kitzinger, London
Printed and bound in Great Britain by Redwood Books,
Trowbridge, Wiltshire

CONTENTS

ACKNOWLEDGMENTS

The authors are pleased to be able to thank Ms Sheena Barbour and Ms Samantha Evans of the Museums Association for the help they gave in the early stages of compiling the original lists for the Internet. It is also a great pleasure to thank Captain C.G. Allen of the National Historic Ships Committee, Mr. John Barrett of the Imperial War Museum, Mr. William J. Mills of the Scott Polar Research Institute and Mr. Jeremy Warren of the Museums & Galleries Commission for their help and encouragement. We are grateful to many individuals who have sent us information about museums and historic vessels, including Mr. Mike Smylie of the 40+ Fishing Boat Association, Mr. Iain Crosbie, Mr. Edwin King and other members of MARHST-L (the Internet's Marine History Information Exchange Group), and also the very many curators and keepers of most of the museums and vessels listed. The steady development of the list, during the past three years on the Internet, would not have been possible without the friendly and efficient assistance of Dr. Glen Segell of Kings College London, who has uploaded each new revision of the list to its Internet web-site in the Mailbase Lists.

INTRODUCTION

This book is a concise listing of most of the naval and maritime museums, collections of maritime interest, and accessible historic vessels in the brittano-hibernian archipelago. It is derived primarily from a list that we have been maintaining on the computer Internet since January 1995. It was put there so that ship enthusiasts, maritime historians, tourists, etc., who had Internet access anywhere in the world, could get some preliminary information about the places where the maritime heritage of these islands was on display. This printed version makes it accessible to those who are not able to, or not interested in using the Internet.

The aim is to provide concise information about the location of a museum or vessel, ways of contacting the administration, and a short summary of what the museum has to offer in terms of its displays and related facilities. It is not intended to be a detailed guide to the displays, collections or facilities.

Where the administrators are at a different address, that postal address is given. Telephone and facsimile numbers are given in the international format of +44 followed by (0) area code and number for addresses in Britain, and +353 (0) etc. for addresses in the Republic of Ireland (Eire). A few museums use higher cost (0839) or (0891) lines for pre-recorded information. These premium code numbers are not accessible from outside the UK. Whenever possible we have listed e-mail addresses and web sites, but Internet users should be aware that in most cases these web sites are unofficial ones that do not give access to the museum; they are often maintained by enthusiasts or tourism agencies, without official approval by the museum. Some of these web sites blossom and fade almost as fast as roses in summer. Regular users of the Internet will be familiar with the use of the searching facilities for locating new web addresses.

Opening times: We only give the days of the week when a museum opens; we make no attempt to list opening hours in detail as these are too variable. Many museums are listed as opening 'Daily'; this generally excludes Christmas Day and New Year and maybe the days between. Opening times may change at short notice, so prospective visitors are strongly advised to get confirmation from the museum's administration shortly before setting off on a journey to a museum.

Admission charges: These are not listed as they are too variable. The old British tradition of free entry to museums is being killed off by commercial pressures and chronic underfunding from official sources. Expect to pay anything from about 50 pence per person at some little museums, to about £8 or more for a 'passport ticket' at a large site with multiple attractions, where there are usually cheaper concessions for children and non-wage-earners. Some museums still allow free access, but depend upon generous voluntary donations at the door to keep going. The situation is constantly changing.

Shops and catering: Almost all large museums have an in-house shop selling books, souvenirs, etc. and the income generated helps the museum. Many museums also have a cafeteria or similar catering facility for light meals. We have not listed this information; contact the museum if it might be important for your visit.

At the end of this book you will find a list of 444 named vessels. This is a sample of the historic vessels in these islands. The list includes the major museum-ships, but it mostly lists smaller named craft, usually part of the collection of one of the museums listed in the main section. A few are 'Not Museum Vessels', indicated by the abbreviation: NMV. These are classic vessels not owned by museums, but which are in private ownership or belong to trusts, and they often operate on a commercial basis. The list is far from comprehensive.

Other Reference and Guide Books

The National Maritime Museum Guide to Maritime Britain, by Keith Wheatley (Webb & Bower: Exeter: 1990. ISBN 0-86350-268-7) is still in print at the time of writing and on sale at the National Maritime Museum and good bookshops. This useful and well illustrated book works its way around the coast of Britain, giving brief information on every museum and location of maritime interest, plus some general maritime history for the area. Unfortunately, inland sites and the Republic of Ireland are not covered.

For those visiting a limited area of Britain, one of the volumes in the series: *Exploring Museums* might be useful (printed by HMSO for the Museums Association and the Museums & Galleries Commission between 1989–93). These volumes give detailed descriptions of the exhibits in all the main museums, not just the maritime ones, within a particular area of the UK and have short summaries of the smaller ones. The series is still in print, but with ten volumes to cover the whole UK, buying a whole set would be expensive!

The *Cambridge Guide to the Museums of Britain and Ireland* by K. Hudson & A. Nicholls (1987/89) is now out of print, and out of date in many of its details, but it was an extensive and well presented guide to museums in general. It might still be of interest if found cheaply in a second-hand bookshop.

The current *Museums Yearbook* (The Museums Association, 42 Clerkenwell Close, London EC1R 0PA) is invaluable for administrative details, but it gives little information about the collections and is not a guide book. It is quite expensive.

Shire Publications Ltd., of Princes Risborough, HP27 9AA, publish a series of inexpensive small books on selected topics. They suggest places to visit and list a bibliography. Recent issues include *Scottish Fishing Boats* by Tanner, *Historic Ships* by Stammers (2nd Ed, 1994), *Canal Barges & Narrow Boats* by Smith (5th Ed, 1994). There are about 15 other inland-waterway and maritime titles still in print but some are getting a bit out of date. *Discovering Maritime Museums and Historic Ships* by Stammers is now out of print. Although published 20 years ago it could still be of interest if found in a second-hand bookshop. Other interesting small books that are now out of print include *Britain's Maritime Heritage* by Veryan Heal and *A Heritage of Ships* by Alexander McKee. The International Congress of Maritime Museums published *A Repertory of Maritime Museums* in 1993 under the

Chairmanship of Dr. M.K. Stammers. (ISBN 0-906367-65-4)
It lists the major maritime museums world-wide and is still available from the National Museums & Galleries on Merseyside.

There are several annual publications that give information about museums, and other places of interest to visitors. These can be useful, but in some cases they only include museums and collections that have paid a listing fee to the publishers.

Useful addresses

Many organisations have information on historic vessels and other aspects of the maritime heritage of these islands. In most cases the full facilities are only available upon membership. These include:

The 40+ Fishing Boat Association of the British Isles. Contacts: Mr. Michael Craine, 63 Birch Hill Crescent, Onchan, Isle of Man IM3 3DA, or: Mr. Mike Smylie, Bron Menai Cottage, Dwyran, Anglesey LL61 6BJ. Tel: +44 (0)1248 430 708.

Archaeological Diving Unit. Scottish Institute of Maritime Studies, University of St. Andrews, St. Andrews, Fife, Scotland KY16 9AJ. Tel: +44 (0)1334 462 919. e-mail: io@st-andrews.ac.uk

Barge Cruising Association. Membership Secretary: Mr. John Griffin, Bossington Wharf, Rothschild Road, Linslade, Leighton Buzzard, Bedfordshire LU7 7TF. Tel: +44 (0)1753 648 112.

Heritage Afloat. Membership Officer & Press Liaison: Mr. Bernard Hales, 9 Strode Street, Egham, Surrey TW20 9BT.

Historic Narrowboat Owners' Club. Mr. C. Deuchar, c/o Nottingham University, Sutton Bonington Campus, Loughborough LE12 5RD. Tel: +44 (0)115 951 6264. e-mail: Chris.Deuchar@nottingham.ac.uk

International Congress of Maritime Museums (ICMM). c/o Norsk Sjøfartsmuseum, Bygdøynesv 37, N-0286 Oslo 2, Norway.

Lighthouse Society of Great Britain. c/o Mr. Ken Trethewey, Gravesend Cottage, Torpoint, Cornwall PL1 2LX. e-mail: kt1@soton.ac.uk

Marine Society. 202 Lambeth Road, London SE1 7JW. Tel: +44 (0)171 261 9535.

Maritime Trust. 2 Greenwich Church Street, Greenwich, London SE10 9BG. Tel: +44 (0)181 858 2698.

Nautical Archaeology Society. c/o 19 College Road, HM Naval Base, Portsmouth, Hampshire PO1 3LJ. Tel: +44 (0)1705 818 419.

Old Gaffers' Association. c/o Brenda Jago, Smugglers Cottage, North Fambridge, Essex CM3 6NA. Tel: +44 (0)1621 741 595.

Railway & Canal Historical Society. 17 Clumber Crescent North, The Park, Nottingham NG7 1EY.

Royal Society of Marine Artists. 17 Carlton House Terrace, London SW1Y 5BD.

Society for Nautical Research. Membership Secretary: Mr. M.P.J. Garvey, Stowell House, New Pond Hill, Cross in Hand, Heathfield, East Sussex TN21 0LX. Tel: +44 (0)1435 863 792.

Steam Boat Association of Great Britain. Secretary: Mr. David
    Beale, Hope Villa, Hatfield Woodhouse, Doncaster
    DN7 6NS. Tel: +44 (0)1603 411 261.
Vintage Wooden Boat Association. c/o Mr. Almer Squires,
    1 Manor Farm Cottages, Common Road, Hopton,
    Diss, Norfolk IP22 2QT. Tel: +44 (0)1953 688381.
World Ship Society. General Secretary: Mr. J.A. Poole, 101
    The Everglades, Duke Meadow Drive, Hemstead,
    Gillingham, Kent ME7 3PZ.

In addition, most museums and museum-ships have a 'Friends'
group and there are many local maritime history and heritage
associations around the coasts of these islands. Some are listed
regularly in periodicals such as *Classic Boat and the Boatman* and
Watercraft, where one can also find advertisements for classic
vessels available for charter, etc.

Information from the World-Wide Web

Although this book is designed primarily for those who have no
access to the computer Internet, museum e-mail addresses and
web sites are listed where appropriate. This has been done to
help those who may already have Internet access, or who get access at a later date. There are many special sites on the Internet
where information is held, and usually updated from time to
time. A few useful general maritime sites are listed below.

The information in this book is drawn mainly from a list of
British and Irish maritime museums that we maintain on the
Internet at:

    http://www.mailbase.ac.uk/lists-f-j/history-sources/files/
    mar-museums.html

The International Council of Museums (ICOM) maintain
Virtual Library Museums Pages. The best connection for British
users is:

    http://www.cs.reading.ac.uk/vlmp/

The primary ICOM site is at:

    http://www.icom.org/vlmp/index.html

From either of these sites, or other mirror sites, one can connect
to thousands of other sites about all kinds of museums all over the
world.

There are a number of sites which are really assemblies of
Internet links to specialised sources of information. These are
generally international in their outlook, though they may have a
preponderance of links to other web sites in their home country.
The Nautical Research Guild, Inc., has a long list of links to
maritime museum and archaeology sites world-wide at:

    http://www.naut-res-guild.org/museum.html

The US Naval & Shipbuilding Museum's site at:

    http://www.uss-salem.org/

has as its primary focus the American cruiser USS *Salem*, but at
the time of writing there are links to over 160 other web sites,
including naval museums, from its Web Links pages, maintained
by Andrew Toppan at:

    http://www.uss-salem.org/links.html

Joseph Poutre maintains a big list of maritime museums around the world, with web links to some of them. About two-thirds of them are in the USA. His list is currently located at:

http://bnj.quxuum.org/navalmus.htm

Two other American web sites have very extensive links to other sites that are largely of interest to mariners:

http://www.mma.mass.edu/campus/library/merch1.htm

http://www.mainelink.net/~drwebb/maritime.html

The Marine Society has a similar set of links for mariners, with a more European bias:

http://www.marine-society.org.uk/

A really outstanding web-site is maintained by Lars Bruzelius in Sweden. It has a strong bias towards maritime history, maritime museums world-wide and famous sailing ships. It has a huge amount of on-site nautical information as well as links to many other sites:

http://pc-78-120.udac.se:8001/

or:

http://pc-78-120.udac.se:8001/WWW/Nautica/ Nautica.html

The steady development of reliable lists of links such as these, together with the emergence of fast searching and indexing 'robots', is transforming the Internet from an anarchic jungle where things were found largely by chance and much effort, to a valuable source of information. Nevertheless, person-to-person exchange is still helpful in directing one towards useful new web-sites.

Disclaimer: while every effort has been made to ensure that the information in this book is accurate, no guarantee can be given and it is possible that some details may have changed by the time the book is published.

ABBREVIATIONS

The following abbreviations are used to indicate facilities that may be available to visitors or used as part of a museum's displays:

ARC: Archives and/or a reserve collection for researchers
AV: Audio Visual aids used in some displays
BA: A facility is only available By Appointment
BH: Bank Holiday (ie Public Holiday), in connection with opening days
DB: A Data Base of information is on site
Edu: Educational facilities can be arranged
GV: Group Visits can be arranged
Lib: There is a Library on site
MM/
IMM: Multimedia/Interactive Multimedia used in displays
NMV: Not a Museum Vessel. In private or commercial ownership
PoW: Prisoner-of-War items, usually of Napoleonic period

The following abbreviations may be used in connection with some telephone numbers:

AH: Telephone number for After-Hours contacts
GV: Telephone number to arrange a Group Visit
SE: Special Events hotline (may be a premium rate service)

LONDON MUSEUMS

HMS Belfast

Morgans Lane, Tooley Street, London SE1 2JH

Write c/o Imperial War Museum, Lambeth Road,
London SE1 6HZ
Phone +44 (0)171 407 6434
Fax +44 (0)171 403 0719
I'net http://www.iwm.org.uk/belfast.htm
http://www.southwark.gov.uk/tourism/attractions/
hms_belfast/
http://www.army.mod.uk/news/museums/details/
m087hmsb.htm
Open Daily

WW2 cruiser, 11,500 ton, 12 x 6in guns. Launched 1938. Much of the original armament still in place. Most of ship open to view, from bridge to boiler & engine rooms, four gun turrets & magazines. Many explanatory videos & AV displays. GV, MM/IMM. Edu BA

Collection of the Worshipful Company of Clockmakers

The Clock Room, Guildhall Library, Aldermanbury,
London EC2P 2EJ

Phone +44 (0)171 606 3030 extn 1865/1866
I'net http://pitcairn.lib.uci.edu/largo/gh/gh_hold.html
Open Mon–Fri ex BH

Collection includes some marine chronometers, 18–20th centuries. Replica of Harrison's First Marine Timekeeper (c1730); his H.5 Longitude Watch (1770); others include Sully (France 1724), Emery (1792) Croucher (1830) and several more recent marine chronometers.

Cutty Sark Clipper Ship

King William Walk, Greenwich, London SE10 9HT

Write The Maritime Trust, 2 Greenwich Church Street,
Greenwich, London SE10 9BG Tel 0181 858 2698;
Fax 0181 858 6976
Phone +44 (0)181 858 3445
Fax +44 (0)181 853 3589

I'net e-mail: cuttysark@greenwichuk.com
http://www.cuttysark.org.uk/
http://www.gmt2000.co.uk/meridian/place/index.htm
orgm0a1.htm
Open Daily

Famous tea clipper. Built 1869 at Dumbarton, on the Clyde. Later in Australian wool trade to 1895. In dry berth since 1954. Wood & iron composite build. Displays of figureheads & China tea trade. Owned by the Maritime Trust. Can be hired for functions.

Gipsy Moth IV

Cutty Sark Gardens, King William Walk, Greenwich,
London SE10 9HT

Write Maritime Trust, 2 Greenwich Church Street,
London SE10 9BG Tel: +44 (0) 181 858 2698
Phone +44 (0)181 858 3445 (This is to the *Cutty Sark*, nearby)
Fax +44 (0)181 853 3589
I'net http://www.netcomuk.co.uk/~endeavor/ships/preserved/
index.html
Open Closed until further notice but outside can always be seen

The ketch, built in 1966, in which Sir Francis Chichester made his solo around-the-world voyage (adjacent to the *Cutty Sark* Clipper Ship, qv).

Imperial War Museum

Lambeth Road, London SE1 6HZ

Phone +44 (0)171 416 5000;
recorded info on 0891 600 140
Fax +44 (0)171 416 5374
I'net e-mail: mail@iwm.org.uk
http://www.iwm.org.uk/london.htm
http://chide.museum.org.uk/imperial.war/
imperial.war.index.html
Open Daily

Naval items include two WW1 15in guns & other historic naval guns. German submarine, Italian 'human torpedo', modern missiles. Large number of paintings. Many items from wars in 20th century: arms, equipment, documents, etc. Special exhibitions. ARC & Lib BA

Lloyd's Nelson Collection

Lloyd's, One Lime Street, London EC3M 7HA

Phone +44 (0)171 327 6260
Fax +44 (0)171 327 6400
I'net http://www.lloydsoflondon.co.uk/heritage/nelson.htm
Open BA only

A collection of correspondence, silver, swords, paintings & other relics commemorating Lord Nelson & the Lloyd's connection. Also material relating to HMS *Lutine* (wrecked 1799 with a cargo of bullion). Her salvaged bell is Lloyd's famous 'Lutine Bell'.

The London Canal Museum

12/13 New Wharf Road, King's Cross, London N1 9RT

Phone +44 (0)171 713 0836
I'net e-mail: martins@popmail.dircon.co.uk
http://www.charitynet.org/~LCanalMus/index.html
Open Tue–Sun & BH Mon

Housed in a mid-19th century ice warehouse is a display of Victorian canal activities: a narrowboat *Coronis*, tools, equipment, photos. The life of canal workers & the cargoes of the London region are illustrated, also history of the ice trade and ice-cream. Edu, GV

Museum in Docklands Project

Warehouse No. 1, West India Quay, West India Docks,
        London

Write c/o Unit C14 Poplar Business Park, 10 Prestons Road,
        London E14 9RL
Phone +44 (0)171 515 1162
    Fax +44 (0)171 538 0209
I'net e-mail: docklands@museum-london.org.uk
Open Proposed opening: January 2000

A new museum of the Port of London & Docklands is to be developed in an 1803 five-storey warehouse, opposite Canary Wharf. Project is to cover London's river, port & people, from Roman times to 20th century, with artefacts, pictures, oral testimony, archives etc.

Museum of London

London Wall, London EC2Y 5HN

Phone +44 (0)171 600 3699
    Fax +44 (0)171 600 1058
I'net e-mail: info@museum-london.org.uk
        http://www.museum-london.org.uk/ (main Museum)
        http://www.molas.org.uk/ (Archaeology Service)
Open Tues–Sun + BH Mon

The Museum is devoted to all aspects of London's society & culture. Some exhibits show evidence of ships & artefacts from London's trade & docklands, from Roman times onwards. ARC, Edu, GV, Lib (BA), MM/IMM

National Maritime Museum

Romney Road, Greenwich, London SE10 9NF

Phone +44 (0)181 858 4422; GVs: 312 6608, Bookshop: 6700,
        Edu: 6747
    Fax +44 (0)181 312 6632; Bookshop: 6632,
        Picture research: 6722
I'net http://www.nmm.ac.uk/
        http://www.army.mod.uk/news/museums/details/
        m090mari.htm
Open Daily

Main British mercantile & naval museum. Paintings, old & new ship models & real boats, instruments, personal items & weapons, guns, flags, charts, dioramas & AV displays illustrate trade, explorers, naval wars, seamanship, nautical archaeology. Edu, Lib. Temp shows.

Steam Tug Portwey

North Quay, West India Dock Road, London E14

Write The Secretary, The Steam Tug *Portwey* Association,
        'Tether's End', Old London Road, Rawreth, Wickford,
        Essex SS11 8UE
Phone +44 (0)1268 769 583
Open NMV: Wed pm or BA with The Secretary

Built 1927, *Portwey* is the last steam-powered, coal-fired, twin screw tug active in the UK. Unique survivor of hundreds of these vessels once working around Britain. Owned by Maritime Trust and chartered to the Association, who preserve & operate her. NMV

Science Museum

Exhibition Road, South Kensington, London SW7 2DD

Phone +44 (0)171 938 8080/8008; Edu: 8222; Library: 8234
  Fax +44 (0)171 938 8118
  I'net http://www.nmsi.ac.uk/welcome.html
  Open Daily

Industrial collection includes many models & some actual marine engines (incl triple-expansion trawler engine). Large collection of ship models from 18th-century Navy Board & PoW to powered naval & merchant ships. Small fishing vessels. Port, diving & navigation displays. ARC BA. GV

St. Katharine's Dock

Located on north bank of Thames, east of the Tower of
      London. Vehicle approach: St Katharine's Way or
      Thomas More Street.

The marina, known as St. Katharine's Haven, is home to a number of classic boats: mainly spritsail Thames barges. All are now in private ownership, used for corporate hospitality etc, but anyone can walk on the quaysides. Sometimes permission is given to view.

PS Tattershall Castle

King's Reach, Victoria Embankment, London
      (between Charing Cross & Westminster Piers)
  Write c/o Mr Terence Prudames, Ship's Engineer, PS
      Tattershall Castle, King's Reach, Victoria Embankment,
      London SW1A 2HR
  Phone +44 (0)171 839 6548
    Fax +44 (0)171 839 1139
  Open NMV: a floating bar/buffet, occasional disco nights.

Side-paddle Humber river ferry. Built 1934, 199ft long, triple-expansion 1200IHP engine (in working order but disconnected & turned electrically for demos). Out of service 1973, was a floating art gallery. Now, after repairs & refurbishment, moored as a 'pub'.

Thames Police Museum

Wapping Police Station, 98 Wapping High Street,
      London E1 9NE
  Phone +44 (0)171 275 4421
    Fax +44 (0)171 275 4490
  Open BA only: apply in writing

Uniforms, equipment & memorabilia of Marine Police Establishment and Metropolitan Police Thames Division. AV, Edu BA

MUSEUMS IN SOUTHERN ENGLAND
SOUTH OF THE WASH

Museums in the counties of:

Berkshire

Blake's Lock Museum, Reading
Gaiety 1887
SL *Nuneham*

Bristol City

Bristol Industrial Museum
Bristol Maritime Heritage Centre
SS *Great Britain*

Buckinghamshire

Beatty Museum, Newport Pagnell

Cambridgeshire

Duxford Airfield (IWM)
Peterborough Museum & Art Gallery
Scott Polar Research Institute Museum, Cambridge

Cornwall

Bude-Stratton Museum, Bude
Cornwall Maritime Museum, Falmouth
Cotehele Quay Museum, Saltash
Mevagissey Folk Museum
Padstow Museum
Royal Cornwall Museum, Truro
St Ives Museum
Trinity House National Lighthouse Museum, Penzance

Devon

Arlington Court, Barnstaple
Brixham Museum
Burton Art Gallery, Bideford
Dartmouth Museum
Hartland Quay Museum
Ilfracombe Museum
Morwellham Quay Open Air Museum, Tavistock
North Devon Maritime Museum, Appledore
Overbecks Museum & Garden, Salcombe
Plymouth City Museum & Art Gallery
Plymouth National Marine Aquarium
Plymouth Naval Base Museum, Devonport
Salcombe Maritime Museum
Smeaton's Tower, Plymouth
Teignmouth Museum
Topsham Museum, Exeter

Dorset

Bridport Harbour Museum
Old Lifeboat House, Poole
Royal National Lifeboat Institution Headquarters, Poole
Waterfront Museum, Poole

Essex

Brightlingsea Museum
Burnham Museum
Mersea Island Museum
National Motor Boat Museum, Basildon
Walton Maritime Museum

Gloucestershire

National Waterways Museum, Gloucester

Hampshire

Buckler's Hard Maritime Museum, Beaulieu
HMS *Collingwood*, Fareham
Emsworth Museum
Hovercraft Museum, Gosport
Naval Ordnance Museum, Gosport
Royal Marines Museum, Southsea
Royal Navy Submarine Museum & Submarine World, Gosport
SS Shieldhall, Southampton
Southampton Maritime Museum

(City of Portsmouth)

Mary Rose
Royal Naval Museum
HMS *Victory*
HMS *Warrior*

Kent

Deal Maritime & Local History Museum
Dolphin Yard Sailing Barge Museum, Sittingbourne
East Kent Maritime Museum, Ramsgate
Historic Dockyard, Chatham
PS *Kingswear Castle*, Chatham
PS *Medway Queen*, Rochester
Rochester Guildhall Museum
Russian Submarine *U475*, Folkestone
Whitstable Museum & Gallery
Whitstable Oyster & Fishery Exhibition

Leicestershire

Foxton Canal Museum, Market Harborough

Lincolnshire

Boston Guildhall Museum

Norfolk

Albion, Ludham
Museum of the Broads, Potter Heigham
Cromer Museum
Cromer RNLI Henry Blogg Museum
Lydia Eva (or in Suffolk)
Lynn Museum
Maritime Museum for East Anglia, Great Yarmouth
Mincarlo (or in Suffolk)
True's Yard Fishing Heritage Centre, King's Lynn
Wells Maritime Museum

Northamptonshire

Canal Museum, Stoke Bruerne

Nottinghamshire
Canal Museum, Nottingham

Oxfordshire
River & Rowing Museum, Henley-on-Thames

Somerset
Admiral Blake Museum, Bridgwater
Fleet Air Arm Museum, Yeovilton
Watchet Market House Museum

Suffolk
HMS *Ganges* Association Museum, Ipswich
International Sailing Craft Association (ISCA) Museum,
    Lowestoft
Lowestoft & East Suffolk Maritime Heritage Museum
Lydia Eva (or in Norfolk)
Mincarlo (or in Norfolk)
MTB 102, Lowestoft
Southwold Museum

East Sussex
Brighton Fishing Museum
Hastings Fishermen's Museum
Newhaven Local & Maritime Museum
Museum of the Royal National Lifeboat Institution,
    Eastbourne
Shipwreck Heritage Centre, Hastings

West Sussex
Marlipins Museum
Selsey Lifeboat Museum

West Midlands
Birchills Canal Museum, Walsall

Wight, Isle of
Bembridge Maritime Museum
Blackgang Sawmill & St Catherine's Quay
Classic Boat Museum, Newport
Cowes Maritime Museum
Fort Victoria Museum, Yarmouth
Sir Max Aitken Museum, West Cowes

Wiltshire
Kennet & Avon Canal Museum, Devizes

Admiral Blake Museum
Blake Street, Bridgwater, Somerset TA6 3NB
  Phone +44 (0)1278 456 127
    Fax +44 (0)1278 444 076
    Open Tues–Sat
Marine paintings & photos, ship models, half-hulls, shipwrights'
tools, nameplate from CSN *Alabama*. Model of Bridgwater dock
in 1900. Diorama of Battle of Santa Cruz. New major exhibition
celebrating 400th anniversary of Robert Blake, born here 1598.
ARC, Edu, GV

Albion

Norfolk Broads: usually Womack Water, near Ludham, Norfolk

Write The Hon Secretary, The Norfolk Wherry Trust, 14 Mount Pleasant, Norwich, Norfolk NR2 2DG

Phone +44 (0)1603 505 815

I'net http://www.ecn.co.uk/e_ed_env_AWherryLegend.htm

Open BA (contact The Secretary); can be chartered.

Albion is the last black-sailed trading wherry on the Norfolk Broads. Built 1898 for inland-waterway transport of large loads. 58ft hull. Loose-footed gaff mainsail on a lowerable 42ft mast, she is the last of a once-common Norfolk vessel. ARC, AV, Edu & GV

Arlington Court

Arlington, Barnstaple, Devon EX31 4LP

Phone +44 (0)1271 850 296

Fax +44 (0)1271 850 711

Open Sun–Fri, April–Oct; also on BH weekends

Among the displays and furnishings of this mansion are good Napoleonic PoW & other ship models; also a sea shell collection.

Beatty Museum

Chicheley Hall, Newport Pagnell, Buckinghamshire MK16 9JJ

Phone +44 (0)1234 391 252

Fax +44 (0)1234 391 388

Open Easter Sun & Mon; May BH Sun & Mon; Sundays + BH Mon in August

Collection of paintings on naval subjects; pictures, memorabilia & personal possessions of Admiral Lord Beatty.

Bembridge Maritime Museum & Shipwreck Centre

Sherborne Street, Bembridge, Isle of Wight PO35 5SB

Phone +44 (0)1983 872 223, 873 125 (24hr)

Fax +44 (0)1983 873 125

I'net http://www.netguides.co.uk/wight/lists/attract.html
http://www.ukonline.co.uk/UKOnline/Regional/
Southern/DO/musiow.htm

Open Daily Mar–Oct, or GV BA

Extensive collection of items salvaged from wrecks: binnacles, engine telegraphs, lamps, bells and hundreds of other objects. Ship models. Displays of local lifeboat, & of HMS *Swordfish*, a submarine sunk in 1940. Display of old & modern diving equipment.

Birchills Canal Museum

Old Birchills, Walsall, West Midlands WS3 8QD

Write c/o Walsall Museum & Art Gallery, Lichfield Street, Walsall, West Midlands WS1 1TR

Phone +44 (0)1922 653 116; AH: 645 778, 653 196

Fax +44 (0)1922 632 824

Open Tue, Wed: am only; Thurs–Sun: pm only.

A display of working life in the past on the Walsall Canal. Includes a reconstructed narrowboat cabin and a weedcutter. The museum is housed in a former Boatman's Rest House.

Blackgang Sawmill & St Catherine's Quay

Blackgang Chine, near Ventnor, Isle of Wight PO38 2HN

Phone +44 (0)1983 730 330
Fax +44 (0)1983 731 267
Open Daily, April–Oct

Replica of a Victorian quayside, with sawmill, boat-building & related crafts. *Liverpool*-class lifeboat *Friendly Forester* (in service 1953–83). Shipwrecks display. The large Blackgang Chine area is a theme park aimed at young people. GV, AV

Blake's Lock Museum

Gas Works Road, Kenavon Drive, Reading,
          Berkshire RG1 3DH

Phone +44 (0)118 939 0918
Fax +44 (0)118 959 0630
Open Daily ex Mon

General displays of Victorian life include features of river & canal life on Reading's waterways. In a Victorian pumping station. Edu.

Boston Guildhall Museum

South Street, Boston, Lincolnshire PE21 6HT

Phone +44 (0)1205 365 954
I'net http://www.hermes2.demon.co.uk/rest.htm
Open Daily, Apr–Sept, Mon–Sat in winter

Maritime room, in this general museum, houses models & Customs artifacts. Associations with Pilgrim Fathers (1607).

Bridport Harbour Museum

The Salt House, West Bay, Bridport, Dorset

Write c/o Bridport Museum Service, South Street, Bridport, Dorset DT6 3NR (Tel: +44 (0)1308 422 116)
Phone +44 (0)1308 420 997
Fax +44 (0)1308 420 659
Open Daily, April–Oct, or BA

Bridport's rope and net-making industries. History of Bridport Harbour, etc. In an old salt-house. (NB There is a separate Museum of Net Manufacture at Bridgeacre, Uploaders, BA. Tel: +44 (0)1308 485 349)

Brightlingsea Museum

1 Duke Street, Brightlingsea, Essex CO7 0EA

Write White Lodge, Ladysmith Avenue, Brightlingsea, Essex CO7 0JD
Phone +44 (0)1206 303 185
Open End March–end October: Mon, Thur, Sat.

A small museum of local maritime history: the Cinque Port Association, the local oyster industry.

Brighton Fishing Museum

201 King's Road Arches, Brighton, East Sussex BN1 1NB

Phone +44 (0)1273 723 064
Fax +44 (0)1273 723 064
I'net http://www.uk-guide.com/s-east/fish-mus.htm
          http://www.brighton.co.uk/tourist/seafront.htm
Open Daily

Paintings, prints, photos & models show the Sussex fishing and pleasure-boat business. Several fishing boats. Working fishermen on-site (fresh catches on sale nearby). DB of fishing families & historical recs. ARC, BA. AV, audio & films; Edu, GV

Bristol Industrial Museum

Princes Wharf, Prince Street, City Docks, Bristol BS1 4RN;

Phone +44 (0)117 925 1470, 922 3571

Fax +44 (0)117 929 7318

I'net http://chide.museum.org.uk/bristol.industrial/ cont..
bristol.industrial.index.html

Open Apr–Oct: Sat–Wed; Nov–March: Sat & Sun.

The Port of Bristol: industrial, maritime & transport history. ARC BA. DB, Edu, GV. Some historic vessels may be moored nearby, but liable to change at short notice. Currently: *Mayflower* (tug), *Pyronaut* & *John King*.

Bristol Maritime Heritage Centre

Wapping Wharf, Gasferry Road, Bristol BS1 6TY

Write Museums Manager, Bristol City Museum & Art
Gallery, Queen's Road, Bristol BS8 1RL

Phone +44 (0)117 926 0680, 922 3571

I'net http://www.ukonline.co.uk/UKOnline/Regional/
SouthWest/DO/museum.htm

Open Daily

Story of Bristol shipbuilding, since 18th century. Ship models, pictures, exhibits formerly in Hilhouse & Hill Collections. Also the ticket issue point for boarding the restored s.s. *Great Britain* (qv). The City Art Gallery has marine paintings. Edu

Brixham Museum

Bolton Cross, Brixham, Devon TQ5 8LZ

Phone +44 (0)1803 856 267

I'net http://www.torbay.gov.uk/history/brimeu.htm
http://www.ukonline.co.uk/UKOnline/Regional/
SouthWest/DO/musdev.htm

Open Mon–Sat, Easter to 31 October. GV BA in winter.

Museum of local history, with much maritime material. Models of local smacks & trawling ketches, displays of shipbuilding, ship's navigational instruments, reconstructed fisherman's cottage. Coastguards, and the story of the Torbay lifeboat since 1866. Edu

The Museum of the Broads

The Broads Haven, Bridge Road, Potter Heigham, Norfolk
Broads (near Great Yarmouth).

Write The Curator, Mr Robert Paul, c/o Ludham Bridge
Services Ltd, Ludham, Norfolk NR29 5NX

Phone +44 (0)1692 630 486, 581 844

Fax +44 (0)181 866 3554

Open Wed–Sun & BH

New museum still being developed. How the Broads began: medieval peat digging, reclamation of marshland, story of the Norfolk keel boats & wherrys, flood control. Broads artefacts & boats, photos, plans, clothing. ARC, AV, Edu, GV, Lib, workshops & demos

Buckler's Hard Maritime Museum

Buckler's Hard Village, Beaulieu, Hampshire SO42 7XB

Write Archives at: The Beaulieu Archive, Beaulieu,
Brockenhurst, Hampshire SO42 7ZN

Phone +44 (0)1590 616 203, 612 345

Fax +44 (0)1590 612 624

I'net http://www.bournemouth.co.uk/ptg/dd003880.htm
http://www.hants.gov.uk/discover/navdef.html

Open Daily

Picturesque village was important 18th century shipyard. Some cottages now recreate life of 18th century shipwright, inn, etc and the museum displays a model of the 18th century village & shipyard, model ships, shipbuilders' tools, original plans, pictures and memorabilia. ARC, Edu GV: BA

Bude-Stratton Museum

The Wharf, Bude, Cornwall EX23 8AG

Write Bude-Stratton Town Council, The Castle, Bude,
Cornwall

Phone +44 (0)1288 353 576

Fax +44 (0)1288 353 576

I'net http://www.ukonline.co.uk/UKOnline/Regional/
SouthWest/DO/muscor.htm

Open Daily, Easter–Sept

Displays include ship models, figureheads, photos and artefacts related to local maritime history, shipwrecks, lifeboats. Also items related to the Bude Canal.

Burnham Museum

The Quay, Coronation Road, Burnham-on-Crouch, Essex
CM0 9AS

Phone +44 (0)1621 783 444

Open Mid-March to 20 Dec: Wed, Sat & Sun.

Part of the collection refers to local maritime history.

Burton Art Gallery

Kinglsey Road, Bideford, Devon EX39 2QQ

Phone +44 (0)1237 471 455

Fax +44 (0)1237 471 455

I'net http://www.ukonline.co.uk/UKOnline/Regional/
SouthWest/DO/museum.htm

Open Tues–Sun

The general collection includes two bone PoW ship models.

Canal Museum (Nottingham)

Canal Street, Nottingham NG1 7ET

Write c/o Nottingham Industrial Museum, Courtyard
Buildings, Wollaton Park, Nottingham NG8 2AE
(Tel: (0115) 915 6870)

Phone +44 (0)115 959 8835, 915 6870

I'net http://www.innotts.co.uk/greensmill/musinfo.html
http://www.british-waterways.com/museum/home.htm

Open Wed–Sun

Models & illustrations showing history, environment & archaeology of River Trent, its tributaries and associated canal system. Edu

The Canal Museum (Stoke Bruerne)

Stoke Bruerne, Towcester, Northamptonshire NN12 7SE

Phone +44 (0)1604 862 229.
  (Independent canal boat trips: 862 107, 862 428)
Fax +44 (0)1604 862 229
I'net http://www.british-waterways.com/museum/home.htm
Open Daily in summer, closed Mon in winter

Shows 200 years of canal history. Replica canal boat, costumes, traditional painted wares, tools, prints, photographs. Housed in restored cornmill; canal locks, boats & Blisworth Tunnel nearby. British Waterways ARC at Llantony Warehouse, Gloucester. Edu BA

The Classic Boat Museum

The Quay, Newport, Isle of Wight PO30 2EF

Phone +44 (0)1983 533 493
Fax +44 (0)1983 533 505, +44 (0)1794 340 708
Open Daily, April–Sept

Collection of about 24 classic small sailing, rowing & powerboats which are still used at events. Two Bembridge Redwings, including Lord Brabazon's auto-gyro *Kestrel*. Chris Craft powerboats including only known Silver Arrow in Europe (*Lady Penelope*). GV, Lib. Edu BA

HMS Collingwood Communications and Radar Museum

HMS *Collingwood*, Newgate Lane, Fareham,
  Hampshire PO14 1AS
  (NB: this is a shore establishment, not a ship)
Write The Museum Curator, Collingwood Maintenance
  Unit, 614 Building, HMS *Collingwood*, Fareham,
  Hampshire PO14 1AS
Phone +44 (0)1329 332 535
Fax +44 (0)1329 332 026
I'net http://chide.museum.org.uk/hms.collingwood/ cont..
  hms.collingwood.index.html
Open Strictly BA. Write to the Curator for appointment.

Important collection of Naval communications, radar, sonar, D/F & testing equipment. Mostly WWII or later. Some enemy & commercial sets. Museum is in the Royal Navy's School of Communications & Weapons Engineering. Lib, ARC, AV, GV– all by appointment.

Cornwall Maritime Museum

2 Bell's Court, Market Street, Falmouth, Cornwall TR11 2AZ

I'net http://www.ukonline.co.uk/UKOnline/Regional/
  SouthWest/DO/muscor.htm
Open Daily April–Oct; closed Sundays in winter.

Displays cover Cornwall & the Sea. Falmouth Packet Service. Ship models, artefacts, paintings. Shipbuilding & navigation. Wrecks & lifesaving. ARC & DB of Cornish-built vessels 1786–1914 BA. NB marine paintings at the Art Gallery. Pendennis Castle is Tudor.

Cotehele Quay Museum

Cotehele Quay, St Dominic, Saltash, Cornwall PL12 6TA

Phone +44 (0)1579 350 830
I'net http://www.nmm.ac.uk/tm/sis.html

Open Daily, April–October.
     Educational programme anytime BA.

The *Shamrock*: Tamar river sailing barge, built 1899, restored in 1970s. Ketch rig, 37 tonnes, 57ft length. Small quayside museum tells story of *Shamrock* & trade on West Country rivers & coast. (Branch of National Maritime Museum, Greenwich, & National Trust)

Cowes Maritime Museum

Library & Maritime Museum, Beckford Road, Cowes,
     Isle of Wight PO31 7SG

Write IoW County Museum & Heritage Service,
     The Guildhall, High Street, Newport PO30 1TY,
     Isle of Wight
Phone +44 (0)1983 293 341
  Fax +44 (0)1983 823 841
I'net http://www.ukonline.co.uk/UKOnline/Regional/
     Southern/DO/musiow.htm
Open Mon–Wed, Fri & Sat.

Collection illustrates former ship-building industry (naval 19th & 20th centuries) and present yacht building industry, with models, photos, plans. Some small craft. Lifeboat material. Photographic archive BA. (also see: Sir Max Aitken Museum at West Cowes)

Cromer Museum

East Cottages, Tucker Street, Cromer, Norfolk NR27 9HB
Phone +44 (0)1263 513 543
I'net http://www.paston.co.uk/users/ncm/cromer.html
Open Daily

Small museum of regional history, with displays on crab fishing. Housed in a renovated fisherman's cottage, garden & wash-house. Illustrations of local coastal trade, and traditional English seaside holidays. Local crab boat.

Cromer RNLI Henry Blogg Museum

The Gangway, Cromer, Norfolk
Write c/o Mr Jim Smith, 33 Hillside, Cromer,
     Norfolk NR27 0HY
Phone +44 (0)1263 512 503
  Fax +44 (0)1263 512 237
Open Daily, May–Oct or BA in winter

Houses the 1935–46 lifeboat *H.F. Bailey*. Displays, models and photographs show the history of the lifeboat station since 1804. The life & medals of Coxswain Henry Blogg. Video films. Edu, GV (Some more lifeboat items are in Sheringham Museum; 4 miles)

Dartmouth Museum

The Butterwalk, Dartmouth, Devon TQ6 9PZ
Phone +44 (0)1803 832 923
I'net http://www.ukonline.co.uk/UKOnline/Regional/
     SouthWest/DO/musdev.htm
Open Mon–Sat (pm only in winter)

Ship models, including French PoW models. Marine paintings and other pictures. Housed in an attractive late-17th century merchant's house.

Deal Maritime & Local History Museum

22 St George's Road, Deal, Kent CT14 6BA

Phone +44 (0)1304 362 837
Open Late May–end Sept: every afternoon

Real & model boats, figure-heads, compasses, stern-boards and relics of the pilots and the lifeboats. The Timeball Tower, on Victoria Parade, is also of maritime interest. GV BA

Dolphin Yard Sailing Barge Museum

Crown Quay Lane, Sittingbourne, Kent ME10 3SN

Write c/o 65 Park Road, Sittingbourne, Kent ME10 1DY
Phone +44 (0)1795 424 132 when open, otherwise 423 215.
I'net http://www.netcomuk.co.uk/~endeavor/ships/preserved/
index.html
Open Sundays & BH, Easter–Oct 31

Small museum specializing in Thames Sailing Barges. Barge models, plans, pictures. Shipwright's, blacksmith's & riggers' tools. Forge & sail-loft. Steam chest & repairs in yard. ARC, Edu, GV. Historic spritsail barge *Cambria* (1906) being restored in basin.

Duxford Airfield (Imperial War Museum)

Duxford, Cambridgeshire, CB2 4QR

Phone +44 (0)1223 835 000;
airfield control: 833 376; SE: 0800 600 900
Fax +44 (0)1223 837 267
I'net http://www.iwm.org.uk/duxford.htm
http://www.webserve.co.uk/clients/saffire/places/
duxford.html
Open Daily

Primarily an aircraft museum, collection includes Fleet Air Arm and US Navy planes & helicopters, and a maritime reconnaissance Avro Shackleton. Other naval items include midget submarine *X-51* & fragment of *X-7*. Education service. Periodic special events.

East Kent/Ramsgate Maritime Museum

Clock House, Pier Yard, Royal Harbour, Ramsgate,
Kent CT11 8LS

Write East Kent Maritime Trust, East Kent Maritime
Museum, Clock House, Royal Harbour, Ramsgate,
Kent CT11 8LS
Phone +44 (0)1843 587 765
I'net http://www.broadstairs.gov.uk/Exploring.html
http://www1.onwe.co.za/titanic/dunkirk.htm
http://www.netcomuk.co.uk/~endeavor/ships/preserved/
index.html
Open Daily, Apr–Sept; Mon–Fri, Oct–March.

Displays of bygone local shipbuilders, sailmakers & fishermen. History of the harbour & Solar Transit Observatory. Navigational instruments, Goodwin Sands. Models of ships & lifeboats. Dunkirk (1940) & *Sundowner* BA. Tug *Cervia* & other historic vessels.

Emsworth Museum

10b North Street, Emsworth (near Havant), Hampshire

Write Emsworth Maritime & Historical Trust, c/o Secretary:
Mrs D Bone, 24 Hollybank Lane, Emsworth,
Hampshire PO10 7UE

Phone +44 (0)1243 373 780 (for Hon. Sec.)

Open Sat, Sun & BH, Easter–end Oct.

Small museum of local history includes maritime material:
photos, prints & mementos. Local yachting & shipping including
models of *Echo*, a large oyster smack, & a Thames barge. Small
library BA. Edu, ARC, GV

Exeter Maritime Museum

Was at: The Haven, Exeter, Devon EX2 8DP. Now closed.
See: ISCA–International Sailing Craft Association, at
Lowestoft

Fleet Air Arm Museum

Royal Naval Air Station Yeovilton, near Ilchester, Somerset

Write Box D6, RNAS Yeovilton, Ilchester, Yeovil, Somerset
BA22 8HT

Phone +44 (0)1935 840 565

Fax +44 (0)1935 840 181

I'net New web-site in preparation.

Open Daily

The history of Naval flying since 1908: 87 aircraft (45–50
displayed, including Concorde 002), many ship & plane models,
weapons, medals & uniforms, paintings & documents.
Collection of c250,000 photos. Search service (c/o Keeper of
Records). AV, Edu. ARC, Lib & GV all BA

Fort Victoria Museum

Fort Victoria Country Park, Westhill Lane, Yarmouth, Isle of
Wight PO41 0RW

Write The Hampshire & Wight Trust for Maritime
Archaeology, Southampton Oceanography Centre,
Southampton, Hants SO17 3HZ

Phone +44 (0)1703 593 290

Fax +44 (0)1703 593 052

Open Daily, Easter–October

The Maritime Heritage exhibition is a small display of artefacts,
pictures, videos & text explaining underwater archaeology.
Housed in part of 19th century coastal fortress, with an adjacent
aquarium. Some archives at the Hampshire & Wight Trust HQ.
AV, Edu, GV

Foxton Canal Museum

Middle Lock, Foxton, Market Harborough, Leicestershire
LE16 7RA

Phone +44 (0)116 279 2657; AH: (0)1858 466 185

Open Daily in summer, Wed–Sun in winter

Boat lift, locks and other items related to canal, 1793–1950. GV

Gaiety 1887

Clewer Boathouse, Clewer Court Road, Windsor, Berkshire

Write French Brothers Ltd, Clewer Boathouse, Clewer Court
Road, Windsor, Berkshire SL4 5JH

Phone +44 (0)1753 851 900, 862 933

Fax +44 (0)1753 832 303

Open NMV: for hire or charter on the Thames. View BA out
of season

Built as the *Oxford* in 1887, with twin compound steam engines.
Renamed *Gaiety*. Later converted to twin diesels. Riveted steel
hull 65ft long, 13.5ft beam. Still in service as a charter or river
tripping boat, after some modernisation.

HMS Ganges Association Museum

Victory House, Shotley Point Marina, Shotley Gate, Ipswich,
Suffolk IP9 1QJ

Write c/o Mr George Athroll, 20 Flint Close, Ipswich IP2 8PU

Phone +44 (0)1473 684 749, 787 291

Open Sat, Sun & BH Mon, Apr–Oct; GV BA

Memorabilia and artefacts of HMS *Ganges*, the RN boys'
training ship, afloat and ashore.

The SS Great Britain

Great Western Dock, Gas Ferry Road, Bristol BS1 6TY

Phone +44 (0)117 926 0680

Fax +44 (0)117 925 5788

I'net http://bristol.park.co.uk/bristguide/docs/ssgreat.html
http://www.epost.co.uk/standards/ssgbrit.html
http://www.pacific-artists.com/steam/museums/
info.htm

Open Daily

Not Brunel's first innovation, but first iron-hulled propeller-
driven transatlantic liner (1843). Salvaged 1970, now undergoing total restoration. Most of exterior, masts, rigging, now
complete. Dining saloon sumptuously restored. Replica engine,
propeller. GV

Hartland Quay Museum

Hartland Quay, Hartland, Bideford, N. Devon EX39 6DU

Write The Old Forge, Woolley, Morwenstow, nr. Bude,
Cornwall EX23 9PP

Phone +44 (0)1288 331 353

Open Daily in Easter week. Daily Spring BH–30 Sept.

Large model of local coast shows over 150 shipwrecks since
Tudor period. Relics of wrecks: steamships *Cingetorix*, *Rosalia*,
Johanna etc, with pictures & documents. Model of vanished 19th
century harbour. Displays of local fishing & trade, smuggling,
lighthouse. GV BA

Hastings Fishermen's Museum

Rock-a-Nore Road, Hastings, East Sussex TN34 3DW

Phone +44 (0)1424 461 446

Open Daily (except Christmas Day)

Housed in the old Fishermen's Church is the last Hastings
sailing lugger *Enterprise* (1912), a horse-capstan, several ship
models including 14ft *Henri Grace A Dieu* and local mementos.
Edu, GV. NB Shipwreck Centre (qv) nearby.

The Historic Dockyard

Dock Road, Chatham, Kent

Write Chatham Historic Dockyard Trust, The Historic
Dockyard, Chatham, Kent ME4 4TE
Phone +44 (0)1634 823 800
Fax +44 (0)1634 823 801
I'net http://www.uk-guide.com/s-east/dockyard.htm
http://www.army.mod.uk/news/museums/details/
m037dock.htm
http://www.pacific-artists.com/steam/museums/
info.htm
Open Daily, Apr–Oct; Wed, Sat & Sun in Feb/Mar/Nov; Shut
Dec & Jan.

Complete Georgian historic dockyard: nine galleries, incl.
Ropewalk, 'Wooden Walls', 'Age of Sail', Ordnance (muzzle-
loaders), Flags. HMS *Gannet* (1878 composite sail/steam sloop)
& HMS *Ocelot* (sub). Lifeboat display. 80 acres so allow four-five
hours. ARC AV Edu GV Lib

The Hovercraft Museum

15 St Marks Road, Gosport, Hampshire

Write The Hovercraft Society, 15 St Marks Road, Gosport,
Hants PO12 2DA
Phone +44 (0)1705 601 310
Fax +44 (0)1705 601 310
Open Enquire.

A collection of about 40 hovercraft of different sizes & models,
including BH7, CC7, HA5, HD1, HM2, SH2, SRN4 & SRN6.
Library of books, periodicals, manuals, plans, pictures, films &
videos BA.

Ilfracombe Museum

Wilder Road, Ilfracombe, North Devon EX34 8AF

Phone +44 (0)1271 863 541
I'net http://www.ukonline.co.uk/UKOnline/Regional/
SouthWest/DO/musdev.htm
Open Daily, Easter–Nov; Mon–Fri am in winter

In the Maritime Room are pictures of local sailing craft, ship
models, a ship-to-shore radio desk. Display on the local lifeboat
and history of the harbour. Other galleries show medals, weapons, aspects of local history, natural history & archaeology.
ARC, Edu

**ISCA Maritime Museum (International Sailing Craft
Association)**

Caldecott Road, Oulton Broad, Lowestoft, Suffolk NR32 3PH

Phone +44 (0)1502 585 606 (Classic Craft: 589 014;
Mobile: (0411) 171 500)
Fax +44 (0)1502 589 014
I'net e-mail: isca.maritimemuseum@btinternet.com
http://www.btinternet.com/~isca.maritimemuseum/
Open Daily

A collection of over 280 craft: historic, classic, ethnographic &
traditional boats. See Appendix for over 80 named vessels. Many
brought to Lowestoft from the Exeter Maritime Museum (now
closed) ARC, GV, Lib, DB of ethnographic craft.

Kennet & Avon Canal Museum

Canal Visitor Centre, The Wharf, Devizes,
  Wiltshire SN10 1EB

Phone +44 (0)1380 721 279, 729 489;
  Crofton: +44 (0)1672 851 639, 870 300
  Fax +44 (0)1380 727 870
  I'net http://www.blacksheep.org/canals/The_Directory/
  canals/
  Open Daily, Feb–Christmas

The exhibition commemorates the pioneer navvies & engineers
who built the 18th century canal between Bristol & Reading, the
traders and others who used and operated the canals, and the
restoration of the almost derelict canal since 1951. Beam engine
at Crofton. Edu

Paddle Steamer Kingswear Castle

The Historic Dockyard, Chatham, Kent ME4 4TQ

Phone +44 (0)1634 827 648
  Fax +44 (0)1634 827 648
  Open NMV: operates public & charter cruises from Chatham
  & Rochester

Britain's last coal-fired paddle steamer. Built 1924 for river excursions. Uses 1904 compound reciprocating steam engine. All
restored to original condition 1971–85. Now in association with
Paddle Steamer Preservation Soc., sails regularly on Medway &
Thames

Lowestoft & East Suffolk Maritime Heritage Museum

Sparrows Nest Park, Whapload Road, Lowestoft,
  Suffolk NR32 1XG

Phone +44 (0)1502 561 963; AH: 511 260
  Open Daily, from May–30 Sept, or GV BA out of season.

Mainly pictures, tools & ship models illustrating local fishing industry in 1920s & 1930s. Housed in former fisherman's cottage,
there is a reconstructed drifter's cabin. Lifeboat material. Associations with Royal Naval Patrol Service. GV, Edu

Lydia Eva (YH 89)

Usually at Great Yarmouth, Norfolk, or Lowestoft, Suffolk.
  (Enquire at Tourist Information or phone (01502)
  677602)

Write c/o Coordinator, *Lydia Eva* & *Mincarlo* Charitable
  Trust, Ketts Acre, Crimpcramp Lane, Wheatacre,
  Beccles, Suffolk NR34 0BQ
  Phone +44 (0)1502 677 602 (Coordinator's residence),
  (0)1603 782 758
  I'net http://www.netcomuk.co.uk/~endeavor/ships/preserved/
  index.html
  Open Usually daily, Easter–Sept or Oct.

Last surviving steam drifter, built 1930, now restored. Usually
open as a museum of the herring fishery, from wheelhouse to fish
hold, net store, crew's quarters & triple-expansion steam engine
(under restoration).

Lynn Museum

Old Market Street, King's Lynn, Norfolk PE30 1NL

Phone +44 (0)1553 775 001 (Answer machine AH); Edu &
 GV: 773 450

Fax +44 (0)1553 775 001

I'net http://kingslynn.finder.co.uk/Free/lynnmuseum.html
 http://www.paston.co.uk/users/ncm/lynn_mus.html

Open Tues–Sat

Part of general collection includes local maritime history. Some
scrimshaw & harpoons reflect Lynn's one-time whaling industry.
Items on Admiral Lord Nelson. Edu, GV. See also Trues Yard.

Maritime Museum for East Anglia

25 Marine Parade, Great Yarmouth, Norfolk NR30 2EN

Phone +44 (0)1493 842 267; archives etc: 855 746

I'net http://www.paston.co.uk/users/ncm/gy_marit.html

Open 2 weeks at Easter, then June-Sept; Daily except Sats

Maritime heritage of Norfolk. Pierhead paintings & naive ship
portraits. Models, tools, pictures & records illustrate herring
fishery, shipping, shipbuilding, inland waterways. Lifeboat items
Captain Manby & lifesaving. Scrimshaw coll. AV Edu GV. Lib &
ARC BA

Marlipins Museum

High Street, Shoreham-by-Sea, West Sussex BN43 5DA

Phone +44 (0)1273 462 994; +44 (0)1243 785 859

I'net http://www.westsussex.gov.uk/leisure/pl/vguid-04.htm

Open Tue–Sun, May–Sept.

Maritime part of collection puts emphasis on ancient port of
Shoreham: ship models & portraits, maps, lifeboats. Edu & GV,
BA. Building is early 12th century, once a Customs House. NB:
West of the harbour entrance are remains of 1850s harbour
defence fort.

The Mary Rose

Mary Rose Trust, College Road, HM Naval Base, Portsmouth
 PO1 3LX

Phone +44 (0)1705 750 521; GV: 839 766;
 Shop & bookshop: 839 938

Fax +44 (0)1705 870 588

I'net e-mail: maryrose@cix.compulink.co.uk
 http://www.compulink.co.uk/~mary-rose/ [UK site]
 http://www.maryrose.org/ [US site]
 http://www.compulink.co.uk/~yama/news95.htm [news
 site]

Open Daily

Henry VIII's warship sank 1545, remains recovered 1982, visible
in preservation ship-hall. Museum shows cannon, Tudor long-
bows & arrows, pottery, wooden & pewter vessels, crew's
clothing, shoes, surgeon's chest, tools etc recovered from wreck.
AV shows, Edu

Medway Queen

Damhead Creek, River Medway, near Rochester, Kent
(contact MQPS for detailed route instructions)

Write *Medway Queen* Preservation Society, 88 Bicknor Road,
Maidstone, Kent ME15 9PB. Phone, Chairman of
MQPS: +44 (0)1622 670 542

I'net http://www.netcomuk.co.uk/~endeavor/ships/preserved/
index.html

Open (NMV) Enquire.

Last surviving Thames Estuary excursion paddle steamer, built
1924. Took part in Dunkirk evacuation, 1940. Compound diag-
onal paddle engine. Vessel was being restored from dereliction,
but has suffered a setback. May possibly be visited. GV BA

Mersea Island Museum

High Street, West Mersea, Colchester, Essex CO5 8QD

Phone +44 (0)1206 385 191; AH: 383 050; Edu: 383 598

Open Wed–Sun & BH, pm only, May–Oct. Opens am on
Special Events

Small museum of local history, with displays of fishing gear &
fisherman's cottage, marine items. Model boats, boat-building
tools. Wildfowling gun-punt (1919). Stowboating. Photos. Edu,
GV

Mevagissey Folk Museum

East Quay, Mevagissey, Cornwall

Write c/o Mrs DJ Hilder (Hon Sec), Turnstones, Chapel
Point Lane, Mevagissey, Cornwall PL26 6PP

Phone +44 (0)1726 843 262

I'net http://www.cornwall-online.co.uk/restormel/
mev-mus.htm

Open Daily, Easter–Sept

The collection, in a boatbuilder's workshop of 1745, is mainly of
local domestic and agricultural items, but includes builders' half-
models, an 'Armada' chest & other artefacts from the local fishing and maritime community.

Mincarlo (LT412)

Usually at Great Yarmouth, Norfolk, or Lowestoft, Suffolk.
(Enquire at Tourist Information or phone +44 (0)1502
677 602)

Write c/o Coordinator, *Lydia Eva* & *Mincarlo* Charitable
Trust, Ketts Acre, Crimpcramp Lane, Wheatacre,
Beccles, Suffolk NR34 0BQ

Phone +44 (0)1502 677 602 (Coordinator's residence);
+44 (0)1603 782 758

Open Usually daily, Easter–Sept or Oct.

A side-fishing trawler, built 1962, with 5 cylinder 500hp diesel
marine engine. Ceased fishing in 1969, she is now being preser-
ved as an example of a near/middle water trawler typical of
1960s.

Morwellham Quay Open Air Museum

Morwellham, Tavistock, Devon PL19 8JL

Phone +44 (0)1822 832 766

Fax +44 (0)1822 833 808

I'net http://www.devon-cc.gov.uk/tourism/pages/attracts/
morwquay.html
http://www.ukonline.co.uk/UKOnline/Regional/
SouthWest/DO/musdev.htm
Open Daily

An old port on River Tamar, important for shipping tin, copper
& arsenic. Village & quays restored, now theme park in style,
with staff in mid-19th century period costume in cottages, workshops and farm. Restored ketch *Garlandstone* & small boats at the
quays. AV Edu

MTB 102

Lowestoft Yacht Harbour

Write MTB 102 Trust, c/o Mr R Basey, Hilltop, Castle Street,
Wroxham, Norfolk NR12 8AB
Phone +44 (0)1603 782 068
Open NMV. Appears at events. Telephone for other
information

Built by Vosper as a prototype Motor Torpedo Boat, 1936–37.
Saw service in WW2, incl the Dunkirk evacuation. Built of Hon-
duras mahogany on Canadian rock elm, 68ft overall, beam 14ft
9in, draft 3ft 9in; ship is substantially original except for new
engines.

National Motor Boat Museum

Wat Tyler Country Park, Pitsea Hall Lane, Pitsea, near
Basildon, Essex SS16 4UW
Phone +44 (0)1268 550 077, 550 088
Fax +44 (0)1268 581 093
I'net http://dialspace.dial.pipex.com/town/terrace/or01/
tradmus.htm
Open Thursday–Monday (daily during school holidays)

Mainly fast sports & leisure craft, the collection of 34 boats
includes *Cygnet*, an 1873 steamer and a 1908 Kelvin engine.
Several hydroplanes, jet boats, offshore powerboats & record-
breakers. Engines, workshop, video room. Library & ARC BA

National Waterways Museum

Llanthony Warehouse, The Docks, Gloucester GL1 2EH
Phone +44 (0)1452 318 054
Fax +44 (0)1452 318 066
I'net http://www.glosibp.co.uk/tt1/areas/glos/glocity6.htm
http://www.british-waterways.com/museum/home.htm
Open daily, except Christmas Day

Models, engines & machinery, hands-on exhibits, illustrate 200
year history of inland waterways. Historic craft at quayside. Boat
trips, horse-wagon tours, crafts displays, cargo handling & stor-
age. AV shows. Shop. British Waterways Archives. Edu

Naval Ordnance Museum

Priddy's Hard Heritage Area, Hardway, Gosport,
Hampshire PO12 4LE
Phone +44 (0)1705 502 490
I'net http://www.hursley.ibm.com/millennium/arms.html
Open Not yet open. Visits sometimes possible BA, or on
special days.

Large naval weaponry: ordnance, torpedoes, mines etc, will be displayed in historic 1771 Grand Magazine, to illustrate the historical development of heavy weapons. Not yet open to public.

Newhaven Local & Maritime Museum

Garden Paradise, Avis Road, Newhaven, East Sussex

Write c/o 51 Hillcrest Road, Newhaven,
East Sussex BN9 9EE

Phone +44 (0)1273 514 760, 516 608

Open Telephone to obtain details.

Photographs & albums of local & general interest. Maritime items. Models of lifeboats & other vessels.

North Devon Maritime Museum

Odun House, Odun Road, Appledore, Bideford,
N. Devon EX39 1PT

Phone +44 (0)1237 474 852

I'net http://www.ukonline.co.uk/UKOnline/Regional/
SouthWest/DO/musdev.htm

Open Daily, May–Sept; pm only: Easter–Apr 30 & October.
Or BA

The maritime history of north Devon. Ship models & half-models, dioramas of medieval shipping, 19th century shipbuilding. Display of tools carved tillers, wrecks & lifeboat rescue, fishing items & WW2 equipment tested locally. Video shows. AV, Edu ARC & GV BA.

SL Nuneham

The Runnymede Boathouse, Windsor Road, Old Windsor,
Berkshire

Write Thames Steam Packet Boat Co., The Runnymede
Boathouse, Windsor Road, Old Windsor, Berkshire
SL4 2SG

Phone +44 (0)1753 840 909

Fax +44 (0)1753 832 303

Open NMV: used for charter & special trips on river. View BA
in winter

Built at turn of the century for Salters of Oxford. Steel hull, 85ft long. Recently restored/rebuilt with near-original Sissons triple-expansion steam engine, new scotch boiler. Now restored to regular charter service, Thames trips & Henley Royal Regatta.

Old Lifeboat House

Fisherman's Dock, East Quay Road, Poole, Dorset BH15 1HZ

Phone +44 (0)1202 663 000

I'net http://www.nmm.ac.uk/tm/sis.html

Open Daily, Easter–end Sept

The lifeboat *Thomas Kirk Wright*, former Poole lifeboat (1938–1962). Damaged during the Dunkirk evacuation, 1940. Historic 19th century lifeboat house holds other RNLI exhibits. (see also the RNLI HQ museum on West Quay Road)

Overbecks Museum & Garden

Sharpitor, Salcombe, Devon TQ8 8LW

Phone +44 (0)1548 842 893
  I'net http://www.ukonline.co.uk/UKOnline/Regional/
    SouthWest/DO/musdev.htm
  Open Sun–Fri, Apr–Jun; daily in July & Aug; Sun–Thur Sept
    & Oct.

There is some maritime material in this collection devoted to
local history etc. Edu. (see also Salcombe Maritime Museum)

Padstow Museum

The Men's Institute, Market Place, Padstow, Cornwall

  Write J Lowe, 8 Cross Street, Padstow, Cornwall
  Phone +44 (0)1841 532 574
  I'net http://www.ukonline.co.uk/UKOnline/Regional/
    SouthWest/DO/muscor.htm
  Open Daily, Easter–Sept

General collection includes features on the local lifeboat, shipbuilding & shipwrecks. Edu

Peterborough Museum & Art Gallery

Priestgate, Peterborough, Cambridgeshire PE1 1LF

  Phone +44 (0)1733 343 329
  Fax +44 (0)1733 341 928
  I'net http://www.demon.co.uk/citygate/441733/attract/
    qa010030.htm
  Open Tue–Sat, except Good Friday and Christmas–New
    Year

The general collection has a local emphasis, and includes several
fine ship models made from bone by French prisoners in the
nearby Napoleonic PoW camp at Norman Cross (1796–1816).
Fenland Lighter Project archives at Peterborough Central
Library.

Plymouth City Museum & Art Gallery

Drake Circus, Plymouth, Devon PL4 8AJ

  Phone +44 (0)1752 304 774
  Fax +44 (0)1752 304 775
  Open Tue–Sat, also BH Mon.

Exhibition 'The City & the Sea' illustrates Plymouth's maritime
history with a good collection of marine paintings & ship models,
including bone PoW models. Edu, GV. Smeatons Tower, The
Elizabethan House and The Merchant House museums are
nearby.

Plymouth National Marine Aquarium

Fishquay, The Barbican, Plymouth, Devon PL4 0LH

  Phone +44 (0)1752 600 301
  Fax +44 (0)1752 600 593
  I'net http://www.national-aquarium.co.uk/
  Open Daily (except Christmas Day)

New aquarium has taken over from the one at the Marine
Biological Association's Laboratories. Large coral, wave and
deep-reef tanks exhibit wide range of fish, marine invertebrates
etc. Captive breeding programmes. Occasional lectures, shows.
Edu, GV

Plymouth Naval Base Museum

HM Naval Base, South Yard, Devonport, Plymouth,
    Devon PL2 2BG

Phone +44 (0)1752 554 582
I'net http://www.cronab.demon.co.uk/pnbm.htm
Open BA: 'phone to arrange guided tour of historic South
    Yard. (GV)

Museum's theme: 'Support for the Fleet', emphasis on victualling. Historic Naval buildings display, shipbuilding crafts &
trades, dockyard artefacts, model ships. Royal Yacht china &
mess gear. Admiralty pattern uniforms, standard measures.
ARC, Lib. DB BA

River & Rowing Museum

Mill Meadows, Henley on Thames, Oxfordshire RG9 1BF

Phone +44 (0)1491 415 600
Fax +44 (0)1491 415 601
I'net e-mail: museum@henrrm.demon.co.uk
    http://www.rrm.co.uk/.
    See old site on http://www.henrrm.demon.co.uk/
Open due to open in Summer 1998

History, ecology & archaeology of the River Thames, the locality
of Henley & the history & sport of international rowing. Collection includes 1812 rowing gig, Saxon logboat, traditional Thames
boats and modern racing shells. ARC, AV, DB, Edu, GV, Lib,
MM/IMM

Rochester Guildhall Museum

High Street, Rochester, Kent ME1 1PY

Phone +44 (0)1634 848 717
I'net http://www.cpoint.co.uk/tw/locales/l119e.html
Open Daily

Extensive exhibits on local history, including ship & boat
models, and bone ones made by French Napoleonic PoWs in
prison hulks on River Medway (reconstruction shown).
Weapons. Associations with Admiral Sir Cloudesley Shovell.
Some silverware on display. AV, GV

Royal Cornwall Museum

Royal Institution of Cornwall, River Street, Truro,
    Cornwall TR1 2SJ

Phone +44 (0)1872 272 205
Fax +44 (0)1872 240 514
I'net e-mail: courtney.rcmric@btinternet.com
    http://www.ukonline.co.uk/UKOnline/Regional/
    SouthWest/DO/muscor.htm
Open Mon–Sat, not BH

Primarily a museum of general local history, with some vessel
models (including lifeboat *Denzil & Maria Onslow*). An important collection of scrimshaw (some BA). ARC DB GV Edu Lib:
all BA

Royal Marines Museum

Eastney, Southsea, Hampshire PO4 9PX

Phone +44 (0)1705 819 385
Fax +44 (0)1705 838 420

I'net http://www.army.mod.uk/news/museums/details/
        m130mari.htm
        http://www.btinternet.com/~pjehome/rm1805.htm
Open Daily

Weapons, uniforms, medals, equipment, photos & paintings,
models, maps & personal items displayed in ten galleries show
the history of Marines since 1664 (Admiral's Regiment) & their
roles on land & sea. RM Commandos, womens' Marens. Special
events. Lib, ARC-BA. Edu

Royal National Lifeboat Institution Headquarters

West Quay Road, Poole, Dorset BH15 1HZ

Phone +44 (0)1202 663 000, 663 043
  I'net e-mail: info@rnli.org.uk
        http://www.rnli.org.uk/
Open Mon–Fri, ex BH

Models, paintings & photos, memorabilia, medals & commemorative items illustrate history of the RNLI. Edu, GV. NB: see
also the Old Lifeboat House, on East Quay.

Museum of the Royal National Lifeboat Institution

King Edward Parade, Eastbourne, East Sussex

Write c/o Captn I. Shearer, RNLI Museum, Wish Tower,
        King Edwards Parade, Eastbourne BN21 4BY
Phone +44 (0)1323 730 717
Open Daily, Apr–Dec

Models of five lifeboats, including early 19th century model of
1789/1810 purpose built lifeboat & 19th century Clovelly model.
Sails & oars of last sailing lifeboat, photos of past lifeboats, their
coxswains & ships given assistance. Personal memorabilia.
Housed in 1898 lifeboat house.

Royal Naval Museum

H.M. Naval Base, Portsmouth, Hampshire PO1 3NH
        (Part of Flagship Portsmouth historic grouping)
Phone +44 (0)1705 727 562 (answer machine AH); 733 060;
        shop: 826 682
  Fax +44 (0)1705 727 575, 875 806
  I'net http://chide.bournemouth.ac.uk/information.office/
        royal.naval.museum.html
        http://www.compulink.co.uk/~flagship/museum.htm
Open Daily, closed Christmas Day.

Britain's main RN museum. Five galleries of models, dioramas,
photos & paintings, medals & personal memorabilia of sailors,
from Lord Nelson to seamen & cabin boys. Navy in 20th century
includes role of Women's Royal Naval Service during WW2.
HMS *Victory* nearby. Redevelopment in progress.

Royal Navy Submarine Museum, and Submarine World

Haslar Jetty Road, Gosport, Hampshire PO12 2AS
        (Research Centre is adjacent at HMS Dolphin)
Phone +44 (0)1705 529 217, 765 130
        Admin, Archs, Resrch: 510 354, 765 250
  Fax +44 (0)1705 511 349
  I'net e-mail: rnsubs@submarine-museum.demon.co.uk
        http://www.submarine-museum.demon.co.uk/
        index.html

http://www.army.mod.uk/news/museums/details/
m062hms.htm
Open Daily, except 24 Dec–1 Jan

AV briefing & tour of HMS *Alliance* (1947). Museum has photos, models, relics & mementos, badges, insignia & medals. Explanation of nuclear power. Periscopes. Diving gear. Outside: *X-24*, *Maiale*, *Biber* miniature subs, torpedoes. *Holland I*. BA: ARC, Edu

Russian Submarine *U475*

South Quay, Folkestone Harbour, Kent CT20 1QH
(was at Long's Wharf, Thames Barrier, Woolwich Road, London)
Phone +44 (0)1303 240 400
Fax +44 (0)1303 240 540
I'net (in course of preparation)
Open Daily

Ex-Soviet Navy, 'Foxtrot' class hunter-killer submarine. 300ft, 2475 tons dived displacement. Carried 22 torpedoes (two low-yield nuclear warheads). 75 crew. Built c1967, decommissioned 1994. *U475* has recently moved to Folkestone from the Thames at London

Salcombe Maritime Museum

Council Hall, Market Street, Salcombe, Devon TQ8 8DE
Write Ms Gwen Dean, Secretary. Address as above.
Open Daily, Easter–31 Oct.

A newly formed museum, holding a superb collection of items of local maritime interest. GV. See also the Salcombe Lifeboat Station Museum, Unity Street. There are also maritime items at nearby Overbecks Museum.

Scott Polar Research Institute

Lensfield Road, Cambridge CB2 1ER
Phone +44 (0)1223 336 540, Librarian: 336 557,
Archivist: 336 555
Fax +44 (0)1223 336 549
I'net http://www.spri.cam.ac.uk/
http://www.cam.ac.uk/CambUniv/RepMuseums/
Scott.html
Open Closed until Autumn 1998, due to building operations.

Material related to exploration and research in polar regions, including 19th century Franklin expeditions & searches, Captain Scott's Antarctic expeditions. Ship models, maps, relics, pictures, scrimshaw, Inuit carvings. Frequent temporary exhibitions. Lib, ARC: BA.

Selsey Lifeboat Museum

Kingsway, Selsey, Chichester, West Sussex.
Write c/o 71 East Beach Road, Selsey, Chichester,
West Sussex PO20 0ES
Phone +44 (0)1243 605 601, 602 833
Open Daily, Easter–Oct. GV: BA

The history & organisation of the RNLI. History of the Selsey Lifeboat Station since 1861 is shown with photographs, models & videos of rescues. Housed in old inshore lifeboat building (the offshore boathouse is always open). Tyne Class Lifeboat *47-001*.

SS Shieldhall

Ocean Village, Southampton, Hampshire

 Write The Solent Steam Packet Company Ltd, S.S. Shieldhall, Ocean Village, Southampton, Hants SO1 1JS
 Phone +44 (0)1703 230 405, 225 853
 I'net http://www.solent.net/shieldhall/menu.htm
 http://www.nauticalbooks.co.uk/shield.html
 Open NMV but open daily. Charter BA. Occasional public
 sailings.

Cargo (sludge) steamship built on River Clyde 1955 to traditional lines: rivetted, teak decks, triple-expansion steam engines.
Twin screw, 268ft oa, 1792GRT. Withdrawn from service 1985,
maintained by Preservation Soc. volunteers. Can be hired, GV,
Edu (all BA)

Shipwreck Heritage Centre

Rock-a-Nore Road, Hastings, East Sussex TN34 3DW

 Phone +44 (0)1424 437 452 (AH: 445 642)
 Fax +44 (0)1424 437 452
 Open Daily, Apr–Oct, or BA for groups

Collection of items from shipwrecks: AD150–19th century.
Audio-visual show. Several nearby wrecks (17th–20th centuries)
can be visited. Edu, GV. NB The Fishermen's Museum (qv) is
nearby.

Sir Max Aitken Museum

83 High Street, West Cowes, Isle of Wight

 Phone +44 (0)1983 295 144, 293 800
 Fax +44 (0)1983 200253
 Open Daily, May–Sept or BA

Sailing memorabilia and paintings. Parts from royal yacht. GV

Smeaton's Tower

The Hoe, Plymouth, Devon

 Write City of Plymouth Museums & Art Gallery,
 Drake Circus, Plymouth PL4 8AJ
 Phone +44 (0)1752 600 608, 304 774
 Fax +44 (0)1752 256 361, 304 775
 I'net http://www.plymouth.gov.uk/
 Open Daily, from Easter–31 Oct. (Edu BA in winter)

The third lighthouse to have been built (1756–59) on the Eddy-
stone Rock. When the present lighthouse was built (1878–82)
the top part of Smeaton's was removed to Plymouth Hoe. Edu,
GV

Southampton Maritime Museum

Wool House, Bugle Street, Southampton,
 Hampshire SO14 2AR

 Write City Heritage Services, Civic Centre, Southampton,
 Hants SO14 7LP
 Phone +44 (0)1703 223 941, 635 904;
 237 584 for archive enqs.
 Fax +44 (0)1703 339 601; 212 048 for archives
 I'net e-mail: GBV6J6AR@IBMMAIL.COM
 http://www.intent.co.uk/southampton/Heritage.html
 http://www.itl.net/vc/europe/Southampton/Tourism/
 heritage.html

Open Daily, ex Mon & BH

Ship models & paintings recall Southampton's maritime past, of sail & steam, dockyards, ship-building & transatlantic liners. Extensive ARC (BA) including photos, harbour & shipbuilders' records, models, ephemera & small boats. Museum is in 14th century warehouse.

Southwold Museum

9–11 Victoria Street, Bartholomew Green, Southwold, Suffolk IP18 6HZ

Phone +44 (0)1502 722 437 (Hon Curator)
Open Daily, Easter–Oct (pm only; am also in August)

A museum of local history, with paintings of shipwrecks, fishing memorabilia, boat models & figureheads. Display on the Battle of Sole Bay (1672). Model of Southwold Lighthouse. Commemorative medals. ARC & Lib BA. GV. See also the Fishermens' Reading Room, nearby.

St Ives Museum

Wheal Dream, St Ives, Cornwall

Write Hon Sec, 20 Trenwith Terrace, St. Ives, Cornwall TR26 1QE
Phone +44 (0)1736 796 005
Open Mon–Sat, occasional Sun, mid May–Oct

Models & mementos of the 1878 –1917 Hain Steamship Co. Photos of Cornish shipwrecks. Clockwork mechanism from Pendeen Lighthouse.

Teignmouth Museum & Historical Society

29 French Street, Teignmouth, Devon TQ14 8ST

Phone +44 (0)1626 777 041; (862 265: Curator AH)
I'net http://www.devon-cc.gov.uk/tourism/pages/ teignm-a.html
http://www.st-andrews.ac.uk/institutes/sims/ deswreck.html
Open Daily

Exhibits include bronze cannon, stone & iron cannon-balls, tools, pottery & other items recovered from offshore 16th century Venetian shipwreck (Spanish Armada?). Displays show local boat-building, the Teignmouth lifeboat & wrecks, WW1 & WW2 memorabilia. ARC, Edu, GV

Topsham Museum

25 The Strand, Topsham, Exeter, Devon EX3 0AX

Phone +44 (0)1392 873 244
Open Mon, Wed, Sat, pm only, Easter–Oct; also Sun Jun–Sept

Local ship-building and merchant voyages are illustrated as part of the displays in this 17th century merchant's house, with a sail loft & estuary gardens. Ship models, tools, anchors, pictures. Edu BA

Trinity House National Lighthouse Museum

Wharf Road, Penzance, Cornwall

Write The Commercial Manager, Trinity House National Lighthouse Centre, Wharf Road, Penzance, Cornwall TR18 4BN

Phone +44 (0)1736 60077
  Fax +44 (0)1736 64292
  I'net http://www.cornwall-calling.co.uk/culture.htm
  Open Daily, Easter–Oct; evenings BA

A reconstructed lighthouse room. Models, optical apparatus, including occulting optic from Coquet & gas-lit optic from Spurn lighthouse. Bells, foghorns & other audible warnings. Buoys, engines & other lighthouse artefacts. Some may be operated. AV theatre. Edu, GV

True's Yard Fishing Heritage Centre

True's Yard, North Street, King's Lynn, Norfolk PE30 1QW

Phone +44 (0)1553 770 479
  I'net http://194.217.46.20/Free/truesyar.html
  Open Daily except Christmas Day

Models of fishing boats (many built by local fishermen), fishing gear, clothing and equipment, displayed in group of restored old cottages. Video, DB, Edu. ARC BA: Extensive arch of docs related to the Wash since 16th century, & many photos. 1904 fishing boat.

HMS Victory

H.M. Naval Base (Historic Dockyard) Portsmouth, Hampshire

Write Flagship Portsmouth Trust, Porter's Lodge, College
     Road, H.M. Naval Base, Portsmouth PO1 3LJ
  Phone +44 (0)1705 861 533; GV: 839 766;
     Marketing: 870 999
  Fax +44 (0)1705 295 252
  I'net http://www.compulink.co.uk/~flagship/victory.htm
  Open Daily

Nelson's flagship at Trafalgar. Tours of 40–45 mins: Nelson's Great Cabin (or Hardy's cabin), the quarterdeck, three gun-decks & orlop, where Nelson died 21 Oct 1805. A few iron cannon with flintlocks; others are lightweight reproductions. In dry berth. Ongoing restoration. AV for disabled. Edu

Walton Maritime Museum

Old Life Boat House, East Terrace, Walton-on-the-Naze,
  Essex

Write c/o Tree House, 10 Walton Road, Kirby-le-Soken,
     Frinton-on-Sea, Essex CO13 0DU
  Phone +44 (0)1255 678 259 (AH)
  Open Daily, pm only, July to Sept., and BH weekends, or BA

Displays of lifeboats, piers, mills, coastguards. Geology of the Naze (fossils, flints; re National Curriculum), local history. Development of the town & its steamers. *City of Leicester* RNLI boarding boat. ARC & GV, BA

HMS Warrior

Victory Gate, H.M. Naval Base (Historic Dockyard),
  Portsmouth, Hampshire PO1 3QX

Phone +44 (0)1705 291 379, GV: 839 766;
     premium info line: (0839) 407 080
  Fax +44 (0)1705 821 283
  I'net http://www.compulink.co.uk/~flagship/warrior.htm
  Open Daily except Christmas Day

Armoured warship (1860). Ship rig & raisable-screw steam power. Restored (Hartlepool) 1979–87. Reproduction Armstrong 110pdr rifled breech-loaders & 68pdr smoothbore muzzle-loaders. Racks of small arms, messes, galley, officer's cabins, cells, laundry, engine-room. Edu & Special Interest Groups BA.

Watchet Market House Museum

Market Street, Watchet, Somerset TA23 0AN

Write c/o M.V. Sully, Secretary, 7 Periton Court, Parkhouse Road, Minehead, Somerset TA24 8AE. (Tel: +44 (0) 1643 707 132)

Phone +44 (0)1984 631 345 (W.H. Norman, Curator),

Open Daily during Easter weekend & May to Sept.

A small general museum with some model ships, figureheads, photos & paintings to illustrate maritime history of the harbour & nautical trade. RNLI exhibits including an original cork lifejacket, paintings & photos. AV, GV

Waterfront Museum

Oakley's Mill, Paradise Street, The Quay, Poole, Dorset

Write Borough of Poole Museum Service, 4 High Street, Poole BH15 1BW

Phone +44 (0)1202 683 138, 661 001 for education answerphone

Fax +44 (0)1202 660 896

Open Daily

On 4 floors of 18th century mill are displays on the maritime history of Poole & its port: fishing, smuggling, boatbuilding, sailmaking, Newfoundland trade. Underwater archaeology: iron age log boat & Spanish wreck. Art includes ship portraits. Edu, AV shows. ARC BA

Wells Maritime Museum

The Old Lifeboat House, West Quay, Wells-next-the-Sea, Norfolk NR23 1AT

Phone +44 (0)1328 711 646; 710 607 for Cox'n of the modern lifeboat

I'net http://www.rnli.org.uk/pages/25.htm

Open Daily, Easter–Sept

The history of the Wells lifeboats, housed in building used as RNLI lifeboat house c1868–1880. Displays on local fishermen: line fishing & shellfish. Storms and floods. GV, Edu BA

Whitstable Museum & Gallery

5a Oxford Street, Whitstable, Kent CT5 1DB

Phone +44 (0)1227 276 998

Fax +44 (0)1227 772 379

Open Mon, Tue, Thu–Sat

Good collection of maritime art, especially ship portraits. Displays on local seafaring: oyster fisheries, early diving. The 1953 floods. The gallery mounts eight special exhibitions every year; 'Whitstable & the Sea' is theme for Oct 10–Dec 5, 1998. AV, GV, Edu

Whitstable Oyster & Fishery Exhibition

East Quay, Whitstable Harbour, Kent CT5 1AB

Phone +44 (0)1227 262 003

Fax +44 (0)1227 264 829
I'net e-mail: bayes@seasalter.eunet.co.uk
Open enquire
Pictures, artefacts & memorabilia show the history of oyster farming & fishing, and the role of science & technology. Edu

MUSEUMS IN NORTHERN ENGLAND
NORTH OF THE WASH

Museums in the counties of:

Cheshire
The Boat Museum, Ellesmere Port

Cumbria
The Beacon, Whitehaven
The Dock Museum, Barrow-in-Furness
Maryport Maritime Museum
Maryport Steamship Museum
Windermere Steamboat Museum

Hartlepool
Hartlepool Historic Quay
Museum of Hartlepool
HMS *Trincomalee*
PSS *Wingfield Castle*

Kingston upon Hull
Ferens Art Gallery
Hull Maritime Museum
Spurn Lightship

Lancashire
Fleetwood Museum
Lancaster Maritime Museum
Lytham Lifeboat Museum

Lincolnshire, North-East
Immingham Museum
National Fishing Heritage Centre, Grimsby

Manchester, Greater
HMS *Bronington*, Manchester
Wooden Canal Boat Society, Ashton-under-Lyne

Merseyside
Historic Warships at Birkenhead
Merchant Navy Museum
Merseyside Maritime Museum, Liverpool
Williamson Art Gallery & Museum, Birkenhead

Middlesbrough
Captain Cook Birthplace Museum, Marton

Northumberland
Grace Darling Museum, Bamburgh
Marine Life & Fishing Heritage Centre, Seahouses

Nottinghamshire
Newark Air Museum

Redcar & Cleveland
Kirkleatham Old Hall Museum, Redcar
Staithes Heritage Centre
Zetland Lifeboat Museum, Redcar

Tyne & Wear
Bede Gallery, Jarrow
HMS *Cavalier*, Hebburn
Newcastle Discovery
South Shields Museum & Art Gallery
Sunderland Museum & Art Gallery
Trinity Maritime Centre, Newcastle upon Tyne

Yorkshire, East
Bridlington Harbour Museum
Goole Museum & Art Gallery
Waterways Adventure Centre & Museum, Goole

Yorkshire, North
Captain Cook Memorial Museum, Whitby
Captain Cook's School-room Museum, Great Ayton
Filey Museum
Whitby Lifeboat Museum
Whitby Museum

Yorkshire, West
Tunnel End Canal & Countryside Centre, Marsden

The Beacon
West Strand, Whitehaven, Cumbria
Write The Beacon Manager, West Strand, Whitehaven,
   Cumbria CA28 7LY
Phone +44 (0)1946 592 302 (Answer machine AH)
Fax +44 (0)1946 599 025
I'net http://www.cumbria-the-lake-district.co.uk/attractions/
   the-beacon.htm
Open Tues–Sun + BH Mon

Whitehaven's social, industrial & maritime heritage. Dioramas &
AV displays illustrate the Georgian port, trade & slavery with America & West Indies, smuggling, fishing. Many ship models, half
hulls & marine paintings. ARC, DB & Lib: all BA. AV, GV, Edu

Bede Gallery
Springwell Park, Butchers Bridge Road, Jarrow,
   Tyne & Wear NE32 5QA
Phone +44 (0)191 489 1807
Fax +44 (0)191 489 1807
I'net http://www.museums.co.uk/j.htm
Open Tue–Fri & Sun

A small museum of local history, with material related to the shipyards.

The Boat Museum

South Pier Road, Ellesmere Port, South Wirral,
Cheshire L65 4FW

Phone +44 (0)151 355 5017
Fax +44 (0)151 355 4079
I'net http://www.british-waterways.com/museum/
ellesmereport/home.htm
http://www.pacific-artists.com/steam/museums/
info.htm
Open Daily in the summer; Sat–Wed in winter

Museum has a collection of over 60 inland waterway boats, from coracles to barges, narrow-boats, ice-boats, tugs & dredgers. Created from dock complex for the Shropshire Union & Manchester Ship Canals it displays many aspects of canal work. ARC, GV, Edu

Bridlington Harbour Museum & Aquarium

Harbour Road, Bridlington, East Yorkshire YO15 2NR

Write Harbour Offices, Gummers Wharf, Bridlington,
Yorks YO15 3AN
Phone +44 (0)1262 670 148
Fax +44 (0)1262 602 041
Open Daily, Easter–Oct, weekends only in winter. Edu BA

Harbour memorabilia. Locally caught fish in aquarium.

HMS Bronington

The *Bronington* Trust, Wharfside, Trafford Park, Manchester

Phone +44 (0)161 877 7778
I'net http://www.ships.co.uk/royalnavy/preserved/index.html
Open Fri–Mon, pm only; Apr–Sept

An ex-RN 'Ton' class minesweeper. Launched 1953, paid off 1988. 360 ton std displacement, converted to minehunter 1963.

Captain Cook Birthplace Museum

Stewart Park, Marton, Middlesbrough, TS7 6AS

Write Dorman Museum, Linthorpe Road, Middlesbrough,
TS5 6LA (Tel & Fax: +44 (0)1642 813 781)
Phone +44 (0)1624 311 211
Fax +44 (0)1624 813 781
I'net http://www.westair-repro.demon.co.uk/mappage/
clevelan.htm
http://www.middlesbrough.gov.uk/museums.htm
Open Tue–Sun + BH Mon.

Cook's early life in this area is illustrated. Displays show his voyages of exploration, and ethnographic material from Australia, New Zealand, Oceania & Canada. AV, GV. Edu, Resource Centre.

Captain Cook Memorial Museum

John Walker's House, Grape Lane, Whitby,
North Yorkshire YO22 4BE

Phone +44 (0)1947 601 900
I'net http://www.hullcc.gov.uk/museums/s-z.htm
http://www.techshop.demon.co.uk/virtual/whitby.html

Open Daily, Apr–Oct; weekends only in March.

Late 17th century harbour-side house attractively restored to period when James Cook lived there as apprentice (1746–49). Prints, models of his ships (all Whitby-built), portrait of Cook (copy) & displays of his voyages & discoveries. Some original documents. GV ARC BA

Captain Cook's School-room Museum

101 High Street, Great Ayton, North Yorkshire

Write c/o Mr D. O'Sullivan, 47 High Street, Great Ayton, Middlesbrough, TS9 6NH (Tel: (01642) 723358)

Phone +44 (0)1642 723 358, 722 208. (AH)

I'net http://www.hullcc.gov.uk/museums/g-l.htm

Open April–Oct: every afternoon; also am Mon–Sat in July & August

A display in the former school where Cook was taught illustrates Cook's voyages, with 19th century maps, items related to Cook & a model of *Endeavour*. A model of the Cook cottage. The village has statue of young James Cook & Obelisk marks site of the cottage. GV, Edu

HMS Cavalier (D73)

At Hawthorn Leslie Yard, Hebburn, South Tyneside, Tyne & Wear; the future of this ship is uncertain at present.

Write c/o Press & Promotions Officer, Town Hall, Westoe Road, South Shields, Tyne-and-Wear NE33 2RL

I'net http://www.hmscavalier.u-net.com/

Open Not open at present.

The last British WW2 period destroyer. *Cavendish* class, launched 1944, tonnage 2106/2530. Since going into reserve in 1972 she has had an unsettled career as a museum ship. Now up for sale again. The HMS *Cavalier* Association is campaigning for preservation.

The Dock Museum

North Road, Barrow-in-Furness, Cumbria LA14 2PU

Phone +44 (0)1229 870 871, 842 311

Fax +44 (0)1229 811 361

I'net http://furness.co.uk/on-line/barrow.htm

Open Wed–Sun.

Displays, some AV, of ship & boat building in Barrow. Collection of 1:48 Vickers ship models, mainly c1900–35. Photographs, navigation instruments. Victorian graving dock. *Watson* class RNLI lifeboat & four other historic boats. ARC BA. GV & Edu BA

Ferens Art Gallery

Queen Victoria Square, Hull, HU1 3RA

Phone +44 (0)1482 613 912

Fax +44 (0)1482 613 913

I'net e-mail: museums@hullcc.demon.co.uk

http://www.hullcc.gov.uk/museums/ferens1.htm

Open Daily

A general art gallery, with a significant collection of marine paintings. (see also the nearby Maritime ('Town Docks') Museum).

Filey Museum

8–10 Queen Street, Filey, North Yorkshire YO14 9HB

Write c/o Tile Cottage, West Avenue, Filey, North Yorkshire
YO14 9BE

Phone +44 (0)1723 513 640

Open Daily ex Sat, June–Sept.

The collection illustrates local life, with emphasis on fishing, the
lifeboat and the seashore.

Fleetwood Museum

Queens Terrace, Fleetwood, Lancashire FY8 5BT (Part of the
Museum of Lancashire, County Museums Service)

Phone +44 (0)1253 876 621

Fax +44 (0)1253 878 088

I'net http://dspace.dial.pipex.com/town/parade/hw22/
fmuse.htm
http://www.pacific-artists.com/steam/museums/
info.htm

Open Good Friday–7 Nov: Thurs–Mon; also Weds, July–
Sept.

Museum in Decimus Burton's 1838 Custom House shows a
model of the docks, a replica trawler bridge, ship models & pictures. Inshore & deep-sea fishing displays. Trawlers in wartime.
History of Fleetwood. Local lifeboat items. ARC, AV/IMM,
DB, Edu, GV, Lib

Goole Museum & Art Gallery

Carlisle Street, Goole, East Riding of Yorkshire DN14 5AA

Write Goole Museums Officer (Janet Tierney), ERYC
Offices, Church Street, Goole DN14 5BG

Phone +44 (0)1405 722 251

Fax +44 (0)1405 722 256

I'net e-mail: Janet.Tierney@east-riding-of-yorkshire.gov.uk
http://www.artguide.org/uk/museumG.html
http://www.hullcc.gov.uk/museums/g-l.htm

Open Mon–Sat (am only on Sat)

Local history museum focusing on development of port, shipyards & community. Ship models, photos & marine paintings,
notably large collection of works by Goole artist Reuben
Chappell. Edu. ARC: (some BA) also in adjacent Local History
Room of Goole Library.

Grace Darling Museum

Radcliffe Road, Bamburgh, Northumberland NE69 7AE

Write Hon Curator, St Aidans Lodge, 2 Radcliffe Road,
Bamburgh, Northumberland NE69 7AE

Phone +44 (0)1668 214 465

I'net http://ourworld.compuserve.com/homepages/ cont...
north_east_england_history_page/Farnesan.htm

Open Daily, Easter–Oct or BA

Personal mementos of Grace Darling, including the rowing
coble used by her and her father to rescue nine survivors of the
Forfarshire, wrecked in a storm in 1838. Pictures, medals, and
items recovered from the wreck. An RNLI museum.

Hartlepool Historic Quay

Maritime Ave, Hartlepool Marina, Hartlepool, TS24 0XZ

Phone +44 (0)1429 860 077
   I'net e-mail: Duncan.Hall@Teesside.btinternet.com
      http://www.teesside-tdc.co.uk/historicquay.html
   Open daily

Modern re-creation of 18th century NE seaport quayside, with naval tailor, weapons shops, naval officer's home, gaol, printers, etc, all with audio. AV programs on Fighting Ships, Pressganged & Seapower themes. See also: Museum of Hartlepool, HMS *Trincomalee*, PS *Wingfield Castle*.

Hartlepool Maritime Museum

Northgate, Headland, Hartlepool: closed. See Museum of Hartlepool

Museum of Hartlepool

Jackson Dock, Hartlepool (Adjacent to Hartlepool Historic Quay)

Write Hartlepool Museum Service, Sir William Gray House, Clarence Road, Hartlepool, TS24 8BT
Phone +44 (0)1429 222 255, 268 916; Edu & GV: 523 609
   Fax +44 (0)1429 869 625
   I'net http://ris.sunderland.ac.uk/museums/hartlepool.htm
   Open Daily

Local history, including fishing, pilotage, lifeboats, ship building. Ship models including builder's half-hulls. Maps, plans & charts. MM. Real sailing coble & displays on the coble type. Harbour & docks. Lens of the old Headland gas lighthouse. PSS *Wingfield Castle* alongside.

Historic Warships at Birkenhead

East Float Dock, Dock Road, Birkenhead, Wirral, L41 1DJ

Write Warship Preservation Trust Ltd., East Float, Dock Road, Birkenhead, Merseyside L41 1DJ
Phone +44 (0)151 650 1573
   Fax +44 (0)151 650 1473
   I'net http://www.ships.co.uk/royalnavy/preserved/index.html
      http://www.netcomuk.co.uk/~endeavor/ships/preserved/index.html
      http://web.ukonline.co.uk/gaz/u-534.html
   Open Daily

Tours of HMS *Plymouth* (*Rothesay* class, Type 12 anti-sub frigate launched 1959) & HMS *Onyx* (*Oberon* class submarine launched 1966). Both vessels served in South Atlantic, 1982. The salvaged German Type IXC/40 U-boat *U534* is open for guided tours BA. AV, Edu, GV

Hull Maritime Museum (was: Town Docks Museum)

Queen Victoria Square, Hull, HU1 3DX

Write Hull City Museums, Ferens Art Gallery, Queen Victoria Square, Hull HU1 3RA
Phone +44 (0)1482 613 902
   Fax +44 (0)1482 613 710
   I'net e-mail: museums@hullcc.demon.co.uk
      http://www.hullcc.gov.uk/museums/towndoc1.htm
   Open Daily

Major displays on near- & far-water fishing, whales & whaling.
Models, pictures, implements & equipment. Whale products,
sounds. Important collection of scrimshaw & Inuit work. Hull
trawlers in WW1 & WW2. Hull's docks. Memorabilia. Lifesaving at sea. ARC BA

Immingham Museum

Margaret Street, Immingham,
        North-East Lincolnshire DN40 1LE

Phone +44 (0)1469 577 066
Open Mon–Sat

Collection covers the relationship between the port and the
railway at Immingham. Archives of Humber Graving Dock
stored.

Kirkleatham Old Hall Museum

Kirkleatham, Redcar, Redcar & Cleveland TS10 5NW

Phone +44 (0)1642 479 500
Fax +44 (0)1642 474 199
Open Tues–Sun & BH Mon–but get confirmation.

Redcar & Cleveland local history including two fishing boats,
items illustrating local fishing, and associated artefacts. Display
of photos on inshore fishing at Redcar. Marine life. *Oakley* class
lifeboat *Sir James Knott* (RNLI). ARC, Edu, GV & Lib–all BA

Lancaster Maritime Museum

Custom House, St George's Quay, Lancaster,
        Lancashire LA1 1RB

Phone +44 (0)1524 64637
Fax +44 (0)1524 841 692
I'net http://dspace.dial.pipex.com/town/parade/hw22/
        fmuse.htm
Open Daily (pm only in Winter). GV BA.

History of the port, with real boats, ship models, displays of
catching local shellfish, whammel boat & inshore fishing. Shipbuilding, trade with West Indies & Baltic. AV displays on port &
the bay. In historic 1764 Custom House, on quay. Edu. GV, Lib
& ARC BA

Lytham Lifeboat Museum

East Beach, Lytham, Lancashire

Write Mr. J.F. Kilroy, 35 Ripon Road, Lytham St Anne's,
        Lancs FY8 4DS
Phone +44 (0)1253 730 155
Open Tue, Thurs, Sat & Sun, May BH–Sept. Also Weds in
        July & Aug.

History of RNLI and Lytham & St Anne's lifeboats shown in
photos; models and mementos. Display on the wreck of the
Mexico, 1886.

Marine Life & Fishing Heritage Centre

8–10 Main Street, Seahouses, Northumberland NE68 5RG

Phone +44 (0)1665 721 257; AH: 720 712
Open Daily, Easter–Oct

Private museum in old mariners' houses near harbour. Displays
of fishing, herring-smoking, lives of local fishermen. Model
ships, navigating instruments, lines, nets, pots & other tools of

the fishermen. Longstone Lighthouse items. Coble. Aquarium.
ARC, Edu

Maryport Maritime Museum

1 Senhouse Street, Shipping Brow, Maryport,
        Cumbria CA15 6AB
  Phone +44 (0)1900 813 738, 815 954
    Fax +44 (0)1900 735 346
  Open Daily in summer; enquire for winter opening.

Models, paintings, tools & other objects illustrate Maryport's
maritime history and shipyards. Paintings by William Mitchell.
Displays for T.H.Ismay (White Star Line) & Fletcher Christian
(of the *Bounty* & Pitcairn). (NB: indep. historic steamships at
Harbour)

Maryport Steamships Museum

Elizabeth Dock, South Quay, Maryport, Cumbria CA15 8AB
  Phone +44 (0)1900 815 954; AH: 813 171
  Open Daily, Easter–October

Friends of the Maryport Steamships Museum maintain 2 vessels: the Scottish harbour tug *Flying Buzzard* (261 tons gross,
built 1951, oil-fired steam), and ex-RN victualling ship *VIC96*
(built 1945). Both were part of the Maryport Maritime Museum
until recently.

Merchant Navy Museum

Albert Dock, Liverpool.

A new museum is due to open here in 1998.

Merseyside Maritime Museum

Albert Dock, Liverpool, Merseyside L3 4AQ
  Phone +44 (0)151 207 0001 (+AH); SE: 478 4499, 478 4747
    Fax +44 (0)151 478 4590
  I'net http://www.nmgm.org.uk/maritime.htm
  Open Daily (Library & Archives: Tues–Thurs, appointment
        advisable)

Galleries devoted to emigration, transatlantic slavery, battle of
the Atlantic, shipbuilding, marine paintings. Display of maritime
crafts. Ship models. Many boats, some stored (view BA). Customs & Excise. Associate vessels at quayside. AV IMM GV Edu
ARC Lib

National Fishing Heritage Centre

Alexandra Dock, Great Grimsby,
        North-East Lincolnshire DN31 1UZ
  Phone +44 (0)1472 323 345
    Fax +44 (0)1472 323 555
  I'net http://education.leeds.ac.uk/~dmclough/jbramley.htm
        http://www.hullcc.gov.uk/museums/g-l.htm
        http://www.nelincs.gov.uk/Pages/Leisure/Venues/
        Heritage.htm
  Open Daily

Paintings, photos, ship models & fishing artefacts illustrate the
life & social history of one of Britain's biggest fishing ports.
Trawlers at War exhibition. Tours of trawler *Ross Tiger*. Four
other fishing boats preserved/restored. ARC & Lib BA. AV DB
Edu GV MM

Newark Air Museum

The Airfield, Winthorpe, Newark, Nottinghamshire

Write Newark (Notts & Lincs) Air Museum Ltd, The Airfield,
Winthorpe, Newark, Notts NG24 2NY
Phone +44 (0)1636 707 170 (24hr answer service)
Fax +44 (0)1636 707 170
I'net http://www.itl.net/vc/europe/Nottingham/Tourism/
newark.html
Open Daily

Six Royal Navy aircraft (Gannet, Sea Hawk, Sea Venom, Sea
Vixen, Buccaneer & Whirlwind helicopter) comprise part of
collection of over 40 aircraft (mainly early military jets). Indoor
displays of engines, radio & radar, instruments, uniforms. ARC
Lib GV. Edu BA

Newcastle Discovery

Blandford Square, Newcastle upon Tyne,
Tyne & Wear NE1 4JA

Phone +44 (0)191 232 6789 (extn 434 for Edu)
Fax +44 (0)191 230 2614
I'net http://www.newcastle-city-council.gov.uk/museums/
http://www.pacific-artists.com/steam/museums/
info.htm
http://www.itl.net/vc/europe/Newcastle/Tourism/
discovery.html
Open Daily

Restored hull of *Turbinia* (1894) dominates entrance. Other ship
& engine models, Parsons material. Maritime gallery shows
models, medieval to cased steamship builder's models (large
Mauretania & HMS *Nelson*), docks. Ryton log boat. RNLI disp.
MM GV, Edu, ARC BA

Sobriety Project: see Waterways Adventure Centre &
Museum

South Shields Museum and Art Gallery

Ocean Road, South Shields, Tyne & Wear NE33 2TA

Write c/o Tyne & Wear Museums, Newcastle Discovery,
Blandford Square, Newcastle-upon-Tyne NE1 4JA
(Tel (0191) 232 6789)
Phone +44 (0)191 456 8740
I'net http://on-tyne.north-east.co.uk/WhatsOn/
museums.asp#SShields
http://ris.sunderland.ac.uk/museums/Southsh.htm
Open Daily, Easter–Oct; Mon–Sat in winter

Displays cover a wide range of local history, including the towns
maritime, lifeboat and naval associations. Edu

Spurn Lightship

Hull Marina, (Old Humber Dock), Castle Street, Hull

Write Hull City Museums, Ferens Art Gallery, Queen
Victoria Square, Hull HU1 3RA
Phone +44 (0)1482 613 902
Fax +44 (0)1482 613 710
I'net e-mail: museums@hullcc.demon.co.uk
http://www.hullcc.gov.uk/museums/spurn1.htm
Open Daily throughout the summer, closed Nov–March

Steel-hulled, manned lightship, built 1927 at Goole, in service until 1975. Length 100ft, 200 tons gross, one 18,000c.p. lantern 35ft above waterline. Crew of 5–7. Was anchored 4.5 miles off Spurn Point at entrance to River Humber 1927–39, 1946–59.

Staithes Heritage Centre

High Street, Staithes, (near Whitby, North Yorkshire)

Write Staithes Heritage Centre, High Street, Staithes,
Saltburn-by-the-Sea, Redcar & Cleveland TS13 5BQ
Phone +44 (0)1947 841 454
Open daily, Mar–Dec, Sat & Sun only in Jan & Feb.

Private museum in quaint fishing village: fishing gear, photos of the 'Steers' fishermen & families, often in local costume. Prints of Captain Cook's last (1776–79) voyage, charts, etc. Archives on local ships, Sanderson records (Cook's 1st employer). Small Lib. AV, GV

Sunderland Museum & Art Gallery

Borough Road, Sunderland, Tyne & Wear SR1 1PP

Write c/o Tyne & Wear Museums, Newcastle Discovery,
Blandford Square, Newcastle-upon-Tyne NE1 4JA
Phone +44 (0)191 565 0723
Fax +44 (0)191 565 0713
I'net http://on-tyne.north-east.co.uk/WhatsOn/
museums.asp#Sunderland
Open Daily

There are marine paintings & large collection of models of sail, steam and motor vessels, especially builders' models. The museum and gallery houses general collections as well. Educational services. ARC BA

Town Docks Museum, Hull: see Hull Maritime Museum

HMS Trincomalee

Jackson Dock, Hartlepool, TS24 0SQ (temporarily dry-docked at adjacent Hartlepool Historic Quay)

Phone +44 (0)1429 223 193
Fax +44 (0)1429 864 385
Open Daily

This frigate, built of teak in Bombay in 1817, was for a time in Portsmouth under the name of *Foudroyant*. Full three-masted ship-rig, 150ft deck length. Built as 38-gun fifth-rate, reduced to 26-gun sixth-rate, 1847. Temporarily in dry dock, still open for tours.

Trinity Maritime Centre

29 Broad Chare, Quayside, Newcastle-upon-Tyne NE1 3DQ

Phone +44 (0)191 261 4691
Fax +44 (0)191 251 1259
I'net http://www.itl.net/vc/europe/Newcastle/Tourism/
maritime.html
http://www.newcastle-city-council.gov.uk/museums/
http://ris.sunderland.ac.uk/museums/trinity.htm
Open Daily, Apr–Oct. Winter: BA. GVs & Edu BA.

Maritime activity on the Tyne shown by builders' & model-makers' ship models. Shipping & quayside equipment, ephemera, navigation instruments. Trinity House uniform. Lifeboat items including reproduction of Grace Darling coble. Diving gear. Memorials. ARC. Independent museum.

Tunnel End Canal & Countryside Centre

Waters Road, Marsden, West Yorkshire HD7 6NQ

Phone +44 (0)1484 846 062

Open Summer: Tue–Sun + BH Mon. Winter: Tue–Thurs, Sat, Sun, BH.

Displays on the Huddersfield Narrow Canal and the Colne Valley.

Waterways Adventure Centre & Museum

Dutch River Side, Goole, East Yorkshire DN14 5TB

Phone +44 (0)1405 768 730

Fax +44 (0)1405 769 868

I'net http://www.hullcc.gov.uk/museums/g-l.htm
http://dialspace.dial.pipex.com/town/terrace/or01/tradmus.htm

Open Daily, Apr–Oct; Mon–Fri in winter

New museum based on community & educational charity teaches the local & social history of transport on Aire & Calder canal system. Model ships & barges, canal tools, personal items. Art gallery on a lighter. Other traditional inland waterway boats. Sobriety project provides work experience. Photos. Edu

Whitby Lifeboat Museum

Pier Road, Whitby, North Yorkshire

Phone +44 (0)1947 602 001

Open Daily, Easter–Oct

The last pulling and sailing lifeboat in service is displayed, together with many models, pictures and memorabilia. RNLI museum.

Whitby Museum

Pannett Park, Whitby, North Yorkshire TO21 1RE

Phone +44 (0)1947 602 908

I'net http://www.spri.cam.ac.uk/lib/museums.htm#uk
http://www.hullcc.gov.uk/museums/s-z.htm
http://www.artguide.org/uk/museumW.html

Open Daily in summer; Tue–Sun, Oct–Apr

Local history: a wing on exploration & whaling. Captain Cook & the Scoresbys. Charts, models of *Baffin, Endeavour, Resolution*, scrimshaw, Pacific ethnography, navigation instruments. Hundreds of ship models from the bizarre to beautiful, including bone PoW work. Lib ARC BA

Whitehaven Museum & Art Gallery

Now closed. Maritime collection at The Beacon, Whitehaven (qv)

Williamson Art Gallery & Museum

Slatey Road, Birkenhead, Merseyside L43 4UE

Phone +44 (0)151 652 4177

Fax +44 (0)151 670 0253

I'net http://www.artguide.org/uk/museumW.html

Open Tue–Sun, pm only, or BA

Some maritime exhibits, particularly on the local ferries, & Cammell Laird, the shipbuilders. Other local maritime history. Most of the gallery displays fine art and pottery. ARC, Edu, GV

Windermere Steamboat Museum

Rayrigg Road, Windermere, Cumbria LA23 1BN

Phone +44 (0)1539 445 565
  Fax +44 (0)1539 445 847, 445 769
  I'net http://www.wwwebguides.com/britain/cumbria/lakes/
      steam.html
      http://www.insites.co.uk/guide/cumbria/attractions/
      steamboat/
  Open Daily, Easter–October

A fine collection of historic powered boats, some salvaged from sunken wrecks and restored to working order. Steam launch *Dolly* (c1850) is oldest powered boat. Many other early steam launches, motor boats, rowing & sailing boats. Trips on lake. ARC BA

PSS Wingfield Castle

Jackson Dock, Hartlepool (Adjacent to Hartlepool Historic
      Quay & Museum of Hartlepool)

  Write Hartlepool Museum Service, Sir William Gray House,
      Clarence Road, Hartlepool, TS24 8BT
  Phone +44 (0)1429 222 255
  Open daily

Paddle steamer, operated as River Humber ferry 1934–74. Now fully restored, in dock where she was built. Triple expansion steam engine and boiler room visible. Bridge fully accessible (wheelhouse is WW2 addition). Display on mid-20th century shipbuilding. Tea room

Wooden Canal Boat Society

Portland Basin, Portland Street South, Ashton-under-Lyne,
      Greater Manchester

  Write Wooden Canal Boat Society, 5 Oaken Clough Terrace,
      Limehurst, Ashton-under-Lyne, OL7 9NY
  Phone +44 (0)161 330 2315
  Open Irregularly, at boat rallies, or BA

The Society collects & restores old canal craft, mostly working boats, with volunteer labour. Six wooden boats at present, from early years of 20th century, in various stages of preservation.

Zetland Lifeboat Museum

5 King Street, Redcar, Redcar & Cleveland TS10 3PF

  Phone +44 (0)1642 486 952, 494 311, 471 813
  I'net http://dspace.dial.pipex.com/town/parade/hw22/
      fmuse.htm
  Open Daily, May–Sept.

An RNLI museum, housing the *Zetland*: built 1802 and the oldest known lifeboat. Other RNLI material on display, plus pictures of old Redcar, fishing equipment and reconstruction of a fisherman's cottage. Collection of model vessels. In 1877 lifeboat house.

MUSEUMS IN SCOTLAND

Aberdeenshire
Arbuthnot Museum, Peterhead
Kinnaird Lighthouse Museum, Fraserburgh
Peterhead Maritime Heritage
Tolbooth Museum, Stonehaven

(Aberdeen City)
Aberdeen Maritime Museum

Angus
Arbroath Museum

Argyll & Bute
The Arctic Penguin Maritime Heritage Centre, Inveraray
Campbeltown Museum

Ayrshire
McKechnie Institute, Girvan
North Ayrshire Museum, Saltcoats
Scottish Maritime Museum, Irvine

Dunbartonshire
Clydebank Museum
Denny Ship Model Experimental Tank, West Dumbarton

Dundee City
Broughty Castle Museum
Discovery Point
McManus Galleries
The Frigate *Unicorn*

Fife
Buckhaven Museum
Scottish Fisheries Museum, Anstruther

Glasgow City
MV *Balmoral*
Museum of Transport
Waverley Paddle-steamer

Highland
Gairloch Heritage Museum
Nairn Fishertown Museum
Wick Heritage Centre

Inverclyde
McLean Museum & Art Gallery, Greenock

Moray
The Buckie Drifter, Buckie
Tugnet Ice House, Fochabers

Scottish Borders
Eyemouth Museum

West Lothian
Linlithgow Union Canal Museum

Aberdeen Maritime Museum

Shiprow, Aberdeen AB11 5BY, Scotland

Phone +44 (0)1224 337 700; Edu: 337 710
Fax +44 (0)1224 213 066
I'net http://www.aberdeen-maritime-museum.co.uk/
introduc.htm
Open Daily

Major new extension, with large model of Murchison oil platform. Aberdeen's relationship with the sea: ship models, paintings, IMM & AV shows illustrate shipbuilding, fishing, oil production. 800 years of the harbour (panoramic views). Special exhibitions. Edu

Arbroath Museum

Signal Tower, Ladyloan, Arbroath, Angus DD11 1PU,
Scotland

Phone +44 (0)1241 875 598; +44 (0)1307 461 460
Fax +44 (0)1307 462 590; +44 (0)1674 671 810
I'net e-mail: cultural@angus.gov.uk
http://www.angus.gov.uk/history/museums/
museums.htm
Open Mon–Sat; also Sunday pm July & Aug

Housed in elegant 1813 shore-station to Bell Rock Lighthouse, the museum illustrates history of local fishing and herring smoking. RNLI and lighthouse material. Other local history, marine life. ARC, AV, Edu, GV

Arbuthnot Museum

St. Peter Street, Peterhead, Aberdeenshire AB42 1QD,
Scotland

Write Aberdeenshire Heritage HQ, Aden Country Park,
Mintlaw, Peterhead, Aberdeenshire AB42 5FQ
Phone +44 (0)1771 622 906 (Heritage HQ)
Fax +44 (0)1771 622 884 (Heritage HQ)
I'net e-mail: general@abheritage.demon.co.uk
http://www.aberdeenshire.gov.uk/nesms.htm
Open Mon–Sat (closed BH)

Models of fishing boats: mid-19th century scaffies to 20th century motor fishing vessels. Models of 19th century trading vessels & whalers. Arctic animals, whaling & related artefacts. Important collection of Inuit art. Temp exhibitions. ARC, including large photo collection. GV

The Arctic Penguin Maritime Heritage Centre

The Pier, Inveraray, Argyll & Bute PA32 8UY, Scotland

Write Inveraray Maritime Heritage Centre, 60 Tradeston
Street, Glasgow G5 8BH, Scotland
Phone +44 (0)1499 302 213
Fax +44 (0)1499 302 213
Open Daily

Built in Dublin (1911) the vessel was converted to schooner rig. Now a floating museum. Displays relate to Clyde ship-building, Scottish emigration, sailors' craft-work, and hands-on exhibits for youngsters. Cinema, shop, educational activities.

MV Balmoral

Write Waverley Excursions Ltd, Anderston Quay,
  Glasgow G3 8HA, Scotland
Phone +44 (0)141 221 8152; +44 (0)1446 720 656
Fax +44 (0)1446 740 675
I'net http://www.style2000.com/p15.html
Open NMV: Open for public or charity excursions, or charter.

Twin screw ferry & excursion ship, launched 1949. 203.5ft o.a.,
736GRT. Twin 6 cyl 600bhp diesel engines. Maintained by
(Registered Charity) the Paddle Steamer Preservation Society
and makes frequent trips & excursions from many UK locations.

Broughty Castle Museum

Broughty Ferry, Dundee, DD5 2BE, Scotland
Write McManus Galleries, Albert Square,
  Dundee DD1 1DA, Scotland
Phone +44 (0)1382 776 121, 436 916, 432 061
Fax +44 (0)1382 432 052
I'net http://www.dundeecity.gov.uk/dcchtml/cofd/
  leisure.html
Open Mon–Thur, Sat; also Sundays pm Apr–Sept.

Displays local 19th century fishing industry. Scotland's best
collection of 1756–1914 arctic whaling memorabilia. Whaling
archives. RNLI display on the Broughty Ferry Lifeboat. Edu,
GV. In a 15th century estuary fort which also has an arms &
armour collection.

Buckhaven Museum

Buckhaven Library, College Street, Buckhaven, Fife, Scotland
Write Kirkaldy Museum & Art Gallery, War Memorial
  Gardens, Kirkaldy, Fife KY1 1YG, Scotland (Tel: +44
  (0) 1592 412 860)
Phone +44 (0)1592 712 192
Fax +44 (0)1592 412 870
Open Mon, Tue, Thu–Sat.

A small museum displaying local history, especially fishing.

The Buckie Drifter

Freuchny Road, Buckie, Moray AB56 1TT, Grampian,
  Scotland
Phone +44 (0)1542 834 646
Fax +44 (0)1542 835 995
Open Daily, April–Oct.

The maritime heritage of Buckie and the Moray Firth. Herring
fishing with steam drifters. Demonstrations and recreated life of
1920s on the quayside. *Oakley* class RNLI lifeboat. Harbour
tours. Edu. See also nearby Peter Anson gallery & Heritage
Cottage.

Campbeltown Museum

Public Library & Museum, Hall Street, Campbeltown, Argyll &
  Bute, Scotland
Write Museums Development Officer, Argyll & Bute Council,
  Library HQ, Highland Avenue, Sandbank, Dunoon,
  Argyll PA23 8PB, Scotland.

Phone +44 (0)1586 552 366/7, +44 (0)1369 703 214, 703 735
Fax +44 (0)1369 705 797
Open Tues–Sat. (Confirm; changes are possible)

Main collection covers archaeology, social & industrial history of Kintyre, including ship models and fisheries items. Maritime collection is being added to. A display focusing on fishing is now in place. ARC

Clydebank Museum

Town Hall, Dumbarton Road, Clydebank, Dunbartonshire
    G81 1XQ, Scotland
Phone +44 (0)1389 738 702
Fax +44 (0)141 951 8275
Open Mon, Wed, Sat, or BA

Museum illustrates local social & industrial history. A part of the collection includes material on ship-building & engineering. AV, Edu, GV

Denny Ship Model Experiment Tank

Castle Street, West Dumbarton, Dunbartonshire G82 1QS,
    Scotland
Write c/o Scottish Maritime Museum, Laird Forge, Gottries
    Road, Irvine, Ayrshire KA12 8QE (Tel: +44 (0) 1294
    278 283)
Phone +44 (0)1389 763 444
Fax +44 (0)1389 743 093
Open Mon–Tues, Fri–Sat.

The world's first commercial experiment tank, built 1883 for the William Denny & Bros Shipyard. GV

Discovery Point

Discovery Quay, Dundee DD2 5BT, Scotland
Phone +44 (0)1382 201 245
Fax +44 (0)1382 225 891
I'net e-mail: dundeeheritage@sol.co.uk
    http://www.rollos.co.uk/discovery.html
    http://www.weblink.co.uk/regional/dundee.html
Open Daily

Royal Research Ship *Discovery*; built for the 1901–4 Antarctic expedition of the RGS & Robert Falcon Scott. Displays, film, AV effects & school facilities aboard & in quay-side centre tell story of the ship & polar exploration. BA: ARC, Edu, GV

Eyemouth Museum

Auld Kirk, Manse Road, Eyemouth,
    Scottish Borders TD14 5JE, Scotland
Phone +44 (0)1890 750 678
Open Daily, Apr–Sep; Mon–Sat in October; closed in winter.

Folk life and fishing museum. A large tapestry commemorates a local fishing disaster of 1881. GV

Gairloch Heritage Museum

Achtercairn, Gairloch, (Wester Ross) Highland IV21 2BJ,
    Scotland
Phone +44 (0)1445 712 287
Open Mon–Sat, Apr–mid-Oct; winter BA

A general museum illustrating the past of Gairloch parish & the region, from earliest times. Displays of restored boats, local lighthouse and importance of fishing. GV, Lib & ARC BA

Kinnaird Lighthouse Museum

Kinnaird Head, Fraserburgh, Aberdeenshire AB43 5DU,
    Scotland

Phone +44 (0)1346 511 022
Fax +44 (0)1346 511 033
I'net http://www.aberdeenshire.gov.uk/museums.htm
Open Daily

Large display of lenses & equipment from Scottish lighthouses at Northern Lighthouse Board's first lighthouse on Kinnaird Castle (1787–1992). Stevenson engineering family. AV, IMM. The Mission to Deep Sea Fishermen in Fraserburgh is of maritime interest.

Linlithgow Union Canal Society Museum

Manse Road Basin, Linlithgow, West Lothian, Scotland

Write 6 Royal Terrace, Linlithgow, West Lothian EH49 6HQ,
    Scotland
Phone +44 (0)1506 671 215
I'net e-mail: nclonie@aol.com
Open Easter–Sept: Sat & Sun pm only, or BA

The story of the canal construction, with photos, displays of tools, documentation. Wildlife of the canal. AV, Edu. Replica canal boats operate from wharf.

McKechnie Institute

Dalrymple Street, Girvan, Ayrshire KA26 9AE, Scotland

Phone +44 (0)1465 713 643
Open Tues–Sat; also Mon in July & Aug.

Amongst the general exhibits are ship models, ringnet fishing artefacts & relics of the SS *Wallachia* which sank in 1895.

McLean Museum & Art Gallery

15 Kelly Street, Greenock, Inverclyde PA16 8JX,, Scotland

Phone +44 (0)1475 723 741
Fax +44 (0)1475 731 347
Open Mon–Sat, except BH & local public holidays. Evening
    GV BA.

Displays on local history, incl shipbuilding, engineering, ropemaking. Models of 19th century ships & Chinese ivory ship models. Material relating to James Watt. Paintings. Regular programme of temporary exhibitions. Materials for children. GV & Edu BA

McManus Galleries

Albert Square, Dundee DD1 1DA, Scotland

Phone +44 (0)1382 432 020, 434 000; GV: 432 020
Fax +44 (0)1382 432 052
I'net http://www.dundeecity.gov.uk/dcchtml/cofd/
    leisure.html
Open Tues–Sat; also BH Mon (except Christmas–Jan 3)

Among the general human history & art collections are ship models & displays of shipping & ship-building. Admiral Duncan

& Battle of Camperdown (1797), life on warship of the time. Whaling items at Broughty Castle (qv). GV, Edu; ARC BA (some at City Archives)

Museum of Transport

Kelvin Hall, 1 Bunhouse Road, Glasgow G3 8DP, Scotland

Write The Director, Glasgow Museums, Art Gallery & Museums, Kelvingrove, Glasgow G3 8AG, Scotland
Phone +44 (0)141 287 2623, 287 2720
  Fax +44 (0)141 287 2692
  I'net e-mail: darryl.mead@museums.glasgow.gov.uk
    http://www.itl.net/vc/europe/Glasgow/Tourism/transport.html
Open Daily except Tuesdays.

The Clyde Room has a huge display of ship models: a few early Board of Admiralty & French PoW models, but mainly large detailed models of powered navy, passenger & cargo vessels; most built on The Clyde. About 800 models & hulls. ARC, Edu, GV, Lib

Nairn Fishertown Museum

Laing Hall, King Street, Nairn IV12 4NZ, Highland, Scotland

Write The Secretary, 2 Lodgehill Park, Nairn IV12 4SA
Phone +44 (0)1667 456 278, 456 798
  I'net http://www.cali.co.uk/highexp/Nairn/Fishtown.htm
Open Mon–Fri, 1 June–30 Sept.

Model fishing boats & photographs show story of local fishing, the fishertown and fisherfolk in late 19th century & early 20th century. Artefacts & memorabilia of line & net fishing. Reconstructed interior of part of a fisherman's cottage. Edu. Tours of the fishertown BA

North Ayrshire Museum

Manse Street, Kirkgate, Saltcoats, Ayrshire KA21 5AA, Scotland

Phone +44 (0)1294 464 174
  Fax +44 (0)1294 464 234
Open Mon, Tue, Thu–Sat.

A collection related to local & social history includes pictures, plans & a model of Ardrossan harbour, models and/or pictures of vessels *Altair, Antares, Baron Ardrossan, Craigvar* & *The Lancing.* Memorial to 358 men lost in HMS *Dasher* disaster, 1943.

Peterhead Maritime Heritage

South Road, Peterhead, Aberdeenshire, Scotland

Write Aberdeenshire Heritage HQ, Aden Country Park, Mintlaw, Peterhead, Aberdeenshire AB42 5FQ (Tel: +44 (0)1771 622 906)
Phone +44 (0)1779 473 000
  Fax +44 (0)1771 622 884 (Heritage HQ)
  I'net e-mail: general@abheritage.demon.co.uk
    http://www.aberdeenshire.gov.uk/museums.htm
Open Daily

A new award-winning museum. Displays on fishing, whaling, marine life, navigation & off-shore oil industry. AV, IMM

Scottish Fisheries Museum

St Ayles, Harbourhead, Anstruther, Fife KY10 3AB, Scotland

Phone +44 (0)1333 310 628

  I'net e-mail: rgwp@st-andrews.ac.uk (via Scottish Inst. Mar. Studies)

    http://dspace.dial.pipex.com/town/parade/hw22/fmuse.htm

Open Daily

Most aspects of Scottish fishing covered, including whaling, salmon & related trades. Many models & paintings, plus 15 full-size boats now in historic boatyard & harbour. Fisherfolk communities & role of Scottish women in fishing trade. Photo arch & Lib BA. Edu, GV

Scottish Maritime Museum

Harbourside, Irvine, Ayrshire, Scotland

  Write Laird Forge Buildings, Gottries Road, Irvine, Ayrshire KA12 8QE

Phone +44 (0)1294 278 283

  Fax +44 (0)1294 313 211

Open Daily, 1 April–31 Oct

Scottish maritime artefacts illustrate specialist knowledge and skills. Annual special exhibition. 1920s shipyard workers' accommodation. Working slipway & workshops, 19th century engine shop. Many historic Scottish vessels, some boardable. ARC/Lib: BA. Edu

Tolbooth Museum

The Harbour, Stonehaven, Aberdeenshire, Scotland

  Write Aberdeenshire Heritage HQ, Aden Country Park, Mintlaw, Peterhead, Aberdeenshire AB42 5FQ

Phone +44 (0)1771 622 906 (Heritage HQ)

  Fax +44 (0)1771 622 884 (Heritage HQ)

  I'net e-mail: general@abheritage.demon.co.uk

    http://www.aberdeenshire.gov.uk/museums.htm

    http://www.demon.co.uk/tourism/nesms/tolbooth.html

Open Daily ex Tues, June–Sept

Displays illustrate history of Stonehaven's links with the sea. Inshore fishing, herring barrel coopering. Housed in Stonehaven's oldest building, a 16th century storehouse which served as County Tolbooth of Kincardineshire from 1600–1767.

Tugnet Ice House

Tugnet, Spey Bay, Fochabers, Moray IV32 7PJ, Scotland

  Write Senior Museums Officer, The Moray Council, Falconer Museum, Tolbooth Street, Forres, Moray IV36 0PH, Scotland

Phone +44 (0)1343 821 644, +44 (0)1309 673 701

  Fax +44 (0)1343 675 863, +44 (0)1309 675 863

  I'net e-mail: 100655.3315@compuserve.com

    http://www.moray.gov.uk/museums/tugnetic.htm

Open Daily, May–Oct

Displays of commercial salmon fishing from the River Spey, the natural history of the Spey, and shipbuilding at Kingston. The Ice House was a very large commercial ice store. AV show. Educational groups BA

The Frigate Unicorn

Victoria Dock, Dundee DD1 3JA, Scotland

Phone +44 (0)1382 200 900

  Fax +44 (0)1382 200 923

  I'net e-mail: rgwp@st-andrews.ac.uk (via Scottish Inst. Mar. Studies)

    http://www.weblink.co.uk/regional/dundee.html

  Open Daily, 1 Apr–31 Oct; weekdays only in winter.

Oldest British-built warship afloat. Launched Chatham 1824, put into reserve & used as training ship. Most of fabric original. An unusual rounded stern. Period roof, fitted when 'in ordinary'. Guns are lightweight reproductions. ARC, AV, GV, Edu, Lib

Waverley Paddle Steamer

Anderston Quay, Glasgow G3 8HA, Scotland

  Write Waverley Excursions Ltd, Anderston Quay, Glasgow G3 8HA

  Phone +44 (0)141 2218152

  I'net http://www.style2000.com/p15.html

  Open NMV: Scheduled pleasure cruises & charter throughout Britain

Launched 1947, 240ft sea-going, side-paddle Clyde steamer. Was coal fired, converted to oil 1980–81. Triple expansion engines. Refitted & operated by Paddle Steamer Preservation Society, now appears at maritime festivals & operates scheduled UK cruises.

Wick Heritage Centre

19/27 Bank Row, Wick, Highland (Caithness) KW1 5EY, Scotland

  Write The Wick Society, 20 Bank Row, Wick, Caithness KW1 5EY, Scotland

  Phone +44 (0)1955 605 393

  I'net e-mail (for admin only): wick@harenet.demon.co.uk

    http://www.harenet.co.uk/nmg/trail/wick.html

  Open Mon–Sat

The Centre includes restored early 20th century fisherman's house. Wick was then major herring port with 6000 fishermen & workers. Lighthouse, mechanism still working. Fishing boats & gear, kipper kiln, coopering, replica harbour, big photo collection, shore radio.

MUSEUMS IN WALES

Museums in the counties of:

Cardiff
Welsh Industrial & Maritime Museum

Ceredigion
Ceredigion Museum, Aberystwyth

Denbighshire
Rhyl Library, Museum & Arts Centre

Gwynedd
Barmouth RNLI Museum
Lleyn Historical & Maritime Museum, Nefyn
Outward Bound Museum, Aberdovey/Aberdyfi
Porthmadog Maritime Museum
Seiont II Maritime Museum, Caernarfon

Monmouthshire
The Nelson Museum, Monmouth

Swansea
Swansea Maritime & Industrial Museum

Barmouth RNLI Museum

Pen-Y-Cei, Barmouth, Gwynedd, Wales
   Write Curator, 8 Ffordd Bro Mynach, Barmouth, Gwynedd
      LL42 1LZ, Wales
   Open Daily, Easter–Sept

Old photographs of the Barmouth Lifeboat and crews. Edu BA.
NB Items from the medieval 'Bronze Bell Shipwreck' are at the
Ty Gwyn & Ty Crwn Museum (Tel: +44 (0)1286 679 098, Fax
+44 (0)1286 679 637)

Ceredigion Museum

Coliseum, Terrace Road, Aberystwyth, Ceredigion SY23 2AQ,
      Wales
   Phone +44 (0)1970 633 088
   Fax +44 (0)1970 633 084
   Open Mon–Sat, Sun during school holidays

Maritime items in this folk life museum include paintings &
photos of sail & steam vessels, charts & navigation instruments,
ship models & other maritime artefacts, including model of local
RNLI lifeboat *John & Naomi Beattie* (1906–32).

Lleyn Historical & Maritime Museum

Old St Mary's Church, Church Street, Nefyn, Gwynedd, Wales
   Write Capt R Rice Hughes, Pen-y-Maes, High Street, Nefyn,
      Gwynedd
   Phone +44 (0)1758 720 270
   Open Daily from mid-July to mid-Sept.

Model ships & lifeboats, maritime paintings and items associated
with the fishing industry of north-west Wales. History of the
Porthdinllaen lifeboat station.

The Nelson Museum & Local History Centre

Priory Street, Monmouth, Monmouthshire NP5 3XA, Wales

Phone +44 (0)1600 713 519
  Fax +44 (0)1600 775 001
  I'net http://www.mresources.co.uk/monmouth/nelson.htm
    http://www.army.mod.uk/news/museums/details/
    m208nels.htm
  Open Daily

A collection of memorabilia associated with Admiral Lord Nelson. Nelson's sword, commemorative china, glassware, silver, printed matter, ms correspondence & medals. Models & naval equipment. A section devoted to fake Nelson 'relics'. Archiv, Lib, Edu, GV

Outward Bound Museum

Outward Bound, Aberdovey/Aberdyfi, Gwynedd LL35 0RA, Wales

Phone +44 (0)1654 767 464
  Open Daily in summer

A few ship models from the discontinued sailing museum can be seen among the general collection of Outward Bound material.

Porthmadog Maritime Museum

Oakley Wharf No. 1, Porthmadog, Gwynedd, Wales

Write c/o Eifion Davies, Gowerian, Ralph Street, Borth-y-Gest, Porthmadog, Gwynedd, Wales (Tel: +44 (0)1766 512 864)
  Phone +44 (0)1766 513 736
  Open Daily in Easter week, and between May BH to 30 Sept, or BA

Ship models, pictures, documents, tools & other equipment show the importance of local shipbuilding, and the export of slate in the fine Porthmadog topsail schooners during 18th–19th centuries.

Rhyl Library, Museum & Arts Centre

Church Street, Rhyl, Denbighshire LL18 3AA, Wales

Phone +44 (0)1745 353 814
  Fax +44 (0)1745 331 438
  Open Mon–Sat

A small museum illustrates social & maritime history of fishing village & holiday resort. Models of local shipping, the lifeboat *Caroline Richardson*, and a photographic collection.

Seiont II Maritime Museum

Victoria Dock, Caernarfon, Gwynedd, Wales

Write Capt. E.A. Jones, Y Swillies, Beach Road, Menai Bridge, Gwynedd LL59 5HD, Wales
  Phone +44 (0)1248 712 528
  Open Daily (pm only), 24 May–21 Sept. (confirmation advisable)

The dredger *Seiont II*. Models & photos illustrate Caernarfon's maritime heritage.

Swansea Maritime & Industrial Museum

Museum Square, Maritime Quarter, Swansea SA1 1SN, Wales

Phone +44 (0)1792 650 351, 470 371, 653 004

Fax +44 (0)1792 654 200

Open Tues–Sun & BH Mon

The maritime material includes ship portraits & other paintings, ship models, mementos of Chilean copper ore trade via Cape Horn, a restored pulling & sail lifeboat. All housed in 1904 warehouse. Lightship & six other historic vessels. ARC BA. Lib, Edu

Welsh Industrial & Maritime Museum

Bute Street, Butetown Dockland, Cardiff CF1 6AN, Wales

Phone +44 (0)1222 481 919

Fax +44 (0)1222 487 252

I'net http://www.cf.ac.uk/nmgw/industr.html
http://www.pacific-artists.com/steam/museums/
info.htm

Open Tues–Sun, plus BH Mondays

A varying display, usually with material related to Welsh marine heritage. From models & small artefacts to real vessels. *Watson*-class RNLI lifeboat *Watkin Williams*, ex-*Anglesey*; steam tug *Sea Alarm*. Edu, ARC & Research Library. An ex-lightvessel nearby. *Now closed, awaiting re-location.*

MUSEUMS IN NORTHERN IRELAND

Museums in the counties of:

Belfast City
Ulster Museum

Londonderry
Derry Harbour Museum

Tyrone
Ulster American Folk Park, Omagh

Down
Ulster Folk & Transport Museum, Holywood

Derry Harbour Museum

Harbour Square, Derry, Co Londonderry BT48 6AF,
Northern Ireland

Phone +44 (0)1504 377 331, 365 151

Fax +44 (0)1504 377 633

Open Mon–Fri

Ship models, half-hulls, maps and pictures related to maritime heritage of Derry. The *Iona Curragh*–1963 reproduction of ancient boat. Prow of the emigrant sailing ship *Minnehaha*. Museum is in 1882 HQ building of Londonderry Port & Harbour Commissioners.

Ulster American Folk Park

Mellon Road, Castletown, Omagh, Co Tyrone BT78 5QY,
      Northern Ireland

Phone +44 (0)1662 243 292/3
   Fax +44 (0)1662 242 241
   I'net e-mail: uafp@iol.ie
         http://www.infosites.net/tourism/topten/folkpark.html
         http://www.omalib.demon.co.uk/famine/emigrdb.html
   Open Daily in summer, Mon–Fri in winter

An outdoor museum of emigration history. Replica Ulster quayside with early 19th century emigrant ship. Part of an extensive
display of furnished original buildings & gallery exhibitions,
interpreting emigrant life in Ulster & North America. AV, MM,
Edu, GV, Lib, DB

Ulster Folk & Transport Museum

Cultra, Holywood, Co. Down, BT18 0EU, Northern Ireland

Phone +44 (0)1232 428 428
   Fax +44 (0)1232 428 728
   I'net e-mail: uftm@nidex.com
         http://www.nidex.com/uftm/
   Open daily

Extensive site. The transport galleries include displays on the
Titanic and some other maritime items. The 1893 schooner
Result & fishing boat *Mary Joseph* on hardstanding nearby.
Museum is developing to cover life in N. Ireland. Edu, Lib, ARC
BA

Ulster Museum

Botanic Gardens, Belfast BT9 5AB, Northern Ireland

Phone +44 (0)1232 383 000
   Fax +44 (0)1232 383 003, 383 103
   I'net e-mail: marshall.mckee.um@nics.gov.uk
   Open Daily

General museum, with important collection of underwater
archaeological material recovered from three Armada wrecks
(1588). Marine paintings, displays on shipbuilding and the sea.

MUSEUMS ON OFF-SHORE ISLANDS

Museums on the islands:

Channel Islands

Castle Cornet, St Peter Port, Guernsey
Fort Grey Shipwreck Museum, St Peter's, Guernsey
The Maritime Museum, St. Helier, Jersey

Cumbrae

Robertson Marine Life Museum, Millport

Islay

Museum of Islay Life, Port Charlotte

Lewis

Museum Nan Eilean, Stornoway

Isle of Man

House of Manannan, Peel
The Nautical Museum, Castletown

The Orkneys

Orkney Wireless Museum, Kirkwall
Scapa Flow Interpretation Centre, Lyness, Hoy
Stromness Museum

Isles of Scilly

Isles of Scilly Museum Association, St Mary's
Valhalla Figurehead Museum, Tresco

The Shetlands

Scalloway Museum
Shetland Museum, Lerwick
Unst Boat Haven, Haroldswick, Unst

Tiree

Skerryvore Museum, Hynish

Castle Cornet

St Peter Port, Guernsey, Channel Islands

Write Guernsey Museums & Galleries, Candie Gardens,
St Peter Port, Guernsey, C.I. GY1 1UG
Tel: +44 (0)1481 726 518
Phone +44 (0)1481 721 657, 726 518; Edu: 723 688
Fax +44 (0)1481 715 177
I'net e-mail: guemg@itl.net
http://www.guernsey.net/~holiday-g/muse.html
Open Daily, Apr–Oct

Newly refurbished maritime gallery, in a fort dating to 13th century. Ship models, tools, diving gear & navigation instruments illustrate 'Maritime Guernsey' theme. Smuggling, privateering, shipbuilding, shipwrecks and the Royal Navy. Military collections nearby. Edu

Fort Grey Shipwreck Museum

Rocquaine Bay, St Peter's, Guernsey, Channel Islands

Write Guernsey Museums & Galleries, Candie Gardens,
Guernsey, Channel Islands. Tel: +44 (0) 1481 726 518
Phone +44 (0)1481 765 036; Education services: 723 688
Fax +44 (0)1481 715 177
I'net e-mail: guemg@itl.net
http://www.guernsey.net/~holiday-g/muse.html
Open Daily, Apr–Oct

Housed in a coastal Martello tower (1804) is an exhibition of items from many naval & merchant vessels wrecked nearby. Survey by underwater archaeology of 1777 wreck of HMS *Sprightly*. Display of navigation & lighthouse items. Cannon from 1807 HMS *Boreas*.

House of Manannan

The Quayside, Peel, Isle of Man

Write Manx National Heritage, The Manx Museum &
National Trust, Douglas Isle of Man (Tel: +44 (0) 1624
648 000, Fax: +44 (0)1624 648 001)
Phone +44 (0)1624 648 000
Fax +44 (0)1624 648 001
Open Daily

New museum has themed 'heritage' tableaux illustrating 'Story
of Mann' from Celtic times to present: replica Viking ship,
herring fishing, Sir William Hillary & lifesaving at sea, episodes
from Trafalgar & other sea battles, steam packet boats. ARC Edu
GV MM

Museum of Islay Life

Port Charlotte, Isle of Islay, Scotland PA48 7UU

Phone +44 (0)1469 850 358, 850 393
I'net e-mail: margot.perrons@wee-mot.demon.co.uk
Open Daily, Easter–31 Oct; Sun pm in winter, or BA

The museum displays the life & times of the islanders & their
crafts. Maritime items include many small objects recovered
from local shipwrecks (including an Armada wreck), flotsam &
jetsam found locally. Brass bells of *Blythville* & a Scandinavian
shipwreck.

Isles of Scilly Museum Association

Church Street, St Mary's, Isles of Scilly (Cornwall TR21 0JT)

(The southernmost maritime museum in the UK proper)

Phone +44 (0)1720 422 337
Open Daily in summer; Weds pm only in winter

HM Customs gig *Klondyke*. Ship models, including steamboat
Britannia (1870s). Shipwrecks: photos & salvage. Wool pictures
by local seamen. Shipbuilding on Scilly: tools, pictures & half-
hulls. ARC, GV BA. Lib includes logs of local ships.

The Jersey Museum

The Weighbridge, St. Helier, Jersey JE2 3NF, Channel Islands

The maritime collection is now in Maritime Museum, New
North Quay

The Maritime Museum

New North Quay Street, St. Helier, Jersey, Channel Islands

(The southernmost maritime museum in the British Isles)

Write Jersey Museums Service, Weighbridge, St. Helier,
Jersey JE2 3NF, Channel Islands (Tel: +44 (0)1534
633300)
Phone +44 (0)1534 811 043
Fax +44 (0)1534 633 301
I'net e-mail: jersmus@itl.net
http://www.itl.net/vc/europe/jersey/tourism/hisatt.html
Open Daily

New museum with innovative displays on all aspects of Jersey's
maritime heritage: shipbuilding, maritime trade, sea-life, etc.
Paintings & photos, ships' fittings, interactive effects. (Most of
the material was previously in The Jersey Museum.)

Museum Nan Eilean

Francis Street, Stornoway, Isle of Lewis HS1 2NF

Phone +44 (0)1851 703 773
Fax +44 (0)1851 704 709
Open Mon–Sat, Apr–Sept; Tues–Sat in winter

There are maritime and fishing themes included in the displays of life in the Outer Hebrides. Before WWI Stornoway was a major herring fisheries port, and before that whaling was important.

The Nautical Museum

Castletown, Isle of Man

Write Manx National Heritage, Manx Museum & National
    Trust, Douglas, Isle of Man IM1 3LY
Phone +44 (0)1624 648 000
Fax +44 (0)1624 648 001
Open Daily, Easter to 30 September

The *Peggy*, an armed schooner-rig yacht, built c 1791. Housed in George Quayle's 18th century house, with a room like a ship's stern cabin. Some memorabilia & a display of sailmaking tools. GV. ARC at Manx Museum Library, Douglas, where there is also a Viking gallery.

Orkney Wireless Museum

Kiln corner, Kirkwall, Orkney Isles KW15 1LB

Phone +44 (0)1856 874 272
I'net http://www.lirona.demon.co.uk/owm.htm
    http://www.army.mod.uk/news/museums/details/
    m196orkn.htm
Open April–Aug, enquire for details.

The late Jim MacDonald's collection of historic radio equipment. Maps, charts & photos of naval wireless communications at Scapa Flow. German wartime radio, featuring U-Boat radio. Italian PoW handicrafts, and their WW2 chapel is nearby. GV

Robertson Marine Life Museum & Aquarium

University Marine Biological Station, Millport,
    Isle of Cumbrae, Scotland KA28 0EG
Phone +44 (0)1475 530 581/2
Fax +44 (0)1475 530 601
Open Mon–Sat, Easter weekend, then June–Sept

Displays show the history of the station, with replica of first research vessel. Geology & oceanography, fish & invertebrates of the Clyde area. Aquaculture & importance of seaweeds in domestic products. Aquarium. The Robertson Reserve Collection.

Scalloway Museum

Main Street, Scalloway, Shetland Islands

Write c/o Mr. J. Nicholson, Fairhaven, Scalloway,
    Shetland ZE1 0TP
Phone +44 (0)1595 880 256, 880 675, 880 608
Open May–Sept (enquire) or BA

A section of this small museum deals with WW2 operations known as 'The Shetland Bus', a seaborne Norwegian Resistance undertaking, assisted by the RN. Photos, maps, listings of missions & vessels. Shetland fishing & whaling history: models, whaling tools.

Scapa Flow Interpretation Centre

Lyness, Hoy, Orkney Islands

Phone Stromness Museum,
    for enquiries: +44 (0)1856 850 025
I'net http://www.greatoutdoors.com/watersports/diving/
    packages/orkney/diving.htm
Open Daily, Mid-May–Oct; Mon–Fri in Winter

The naval history of Scapa Flow during two World Wars

Shetland Museum

Shetland Museum Service, Lower Hillhead, Lerwick,
    Shetland ZE1 0EL

Phone +44 (0)1595 695 057
Fax +44 (0)1595 696 729
I'net e-mail: shetland.museum@zetnet.co.uk
    http://www.shetland-times.co.uk/visitor/culture.htm
    http://www.shetland-times.co.uk/visitor/lerwick.htm
Open Mon–Sat

Collection includes fine models of a sixern & other Shetland fishing boats, shipbuilders' models & tools, wreck artefacts, sailors' personal items & material related to Arctic & Antarctic whaling. Eskimo work. Restored Ness Yoal *Maggie* (1901) etc. ARC, Edu

Skerryvore Museum

Hynish, Isle of Tiree, Argyll, Scotland

Write c/o Hebridean Trust, 75a Banbury Road,
    Oxford OX2 6PE (Tel: +44 (0) 1865 311 468,
    fax: +44 (0) 1865 311 593)
Phone +44 (0)1879 220 691 (Mrs C. MacFarlane)
Open Enquire at 2 Upper Square, Hynish, if museum is not
    open

A small museum, housed in the Signal Tower, tells the story of the building of the Skerryvore Lighthouse in the 1840s, by Alan Stevenson. He was son of Robert Stevenson the Scottish lighthouse engineer, and uncle to the writer Robert Louis Stevenson.

Stromness Museum

52 Alfred Street, Stromness, Orkney Islands KW16 3DF

Phone +44 (0)1856 850 025
Fax +44 (0)1856 871 560
I'net http://www.spri.cam.ac.uk/lib/museums.htm#uk
Open Daily, May–Sept; Mon–Sat, Oct–April.

Maritime & natural history of Orkney. Lighthouse & ship models including PoW work. Inuit items. Exhibits on Arctic whaling, boatbuilding, fishing. Photos. Scapa Flow & German Battlefleet of WW1. Display on Hudson's Bay Company & the explorations of John Rae. ARC, GV

Unst Boat Haven

Haroldswick, Unst, Shetland Isles, ZE2 9ED

(The northernmost maritime museum in the British Isles)

Write Unst Heritage Centre Trust, c/o Duncan Sandison,
    Wasterpark, Baltasound, Shetland ZE2 9DS
Phone +44 (0)1957 711 324
I'net http://www.shetland-times.co.uk/visitor/unstheri.htm
Open Every afternoon, 1 May–30 Sept. or BA

Sixteen traditional Shetland boats, mostly 1880s–1915. Displayed on a gravel 'beach', with period fishing gear, tools, photos, plans & charts in new (1994) building. Links with Norse vessels shown. The *Far Haaf* replica sixareen sails at Baltasound.

Valhalla Figurehead Museum

Tresco Abbey Gardens, Tresco, Isles of Scilly TR24 0QH

Write c/o National Maritime Museum, Romney Road,
      Greenwich, London SE10
Phone +44 (0)1720 422 849, 422 818
  Fax +44 (0)1720 422 106
  I'net http://www.nmm.ac.uk/tm/sis.html
  Open Daily, Apr–Oct

Collection of 30 ships' figureheads, name-boards & other decorative ships' carvings from the age of sail. Collection was started c1840, from local shipwrecks.

MUSEUMS IN THE REPUBLIC OF IRELAND

Museums in the counties of:

Cork

1796 Bantry French Armada Centre,
Cobh Museum
Irish Naval Service Museum, Haulbowline
The Mizen Vision, Goleen
The Queenstown Story, Cobh

Donegal

Greencastle Maritime Museum

Dublin

National Maritime Museum of Ireland, Dun Laoghaire
Waterways Visitor Centre

Kerry

The Skellig Experience Heritage Centre, Valentia

Limerick

Limerick Museum

Wexford

Kilmore Quay Maritime Museum

Wicklow

Arklow Maritime Museum

Arklow Maritime Museum

St. Mary's Road, Arklow, Co. Wicklow, Republic of Ireland

Phone +353 (0)402 32868
  I'net http://www.rnli.org.uk/pages/198.htm
        http://www.elsas.demon.nl/ierland.htm
  Open Mon–Sat, May–Sept; Mon–Fri in winter

Maritime history of Arklow illustrated by paintings (several by Reuben Chappell), many ship models, navigation & safety equipment, shipwrights' tools & general nautical memorabilia. Display on the torpedoing of the *Lusitania*. Archives include photos BA. Edu & GV BA

1796 Bantry French Armada Exhibition Centre

East Stables, Bantry House, Bantry, Co. Cork,
      Republic of Ireland
  Phone +353 (0)27 51796, 51996
    Fax +353 (0)27 51309, 50795
    I'net http://www.cork-guide.ie/btry1796.htm
        http://www.foundmark.com/Great/Westcork2.html
        http://www.elsas.demon.nl/ierland.htm
  Open Daily, April–Oct

Large cut-away model of French frigate *La Surveillante* forms centrepiece of exhibition describing Wolfe Tone's abortive attempt to expel the English from Ireland, 1796–97. Edu, GV, ARC

Cobh Museum

High Road, Cobh, Co. Cork, Republic of Ireland
  Write Ms Heather Bird, Ballydulea, Cobh, Co. Cork,
      Republic of Ireland
  Phone +353 (0)21 814 240. AH: 811 260
    I'net http://www.elsas.demon.nl/ierland.htm
  Open Daily, Easter–November

Displays of local social life include model ships, Cunard & other maritime memorabilia. Photographs of the US Naval Force in Cork Harbour, 1917. Museum is in the former Presbyterian ('Scots') Church. GV, Edu & Research facilities.

Greencastle Maritime Museum

Greencastle, Inishowen, Co. Donegal, Republic of Ireland
  Phone +353 (0)77 81363
    I'net http://www.elsas.demon.nl/ierland.htm
        http://www.ireland.travel.ie/fi/Index.asp
  Open June–Sept

Ship models, paintings & photos. A traditional Fanad curragh & a wildfowling punt with swivel gun. A rocket cart used for saving survivors of shipwrecks. Other maritime memorabilia.

Irish Naval Service Museum

Haulbowline Naval Base, Ringaskiddy, Co Cork,
      Republic of Ireland
  Phone +353 (0)21 378 777; Direct line to Lt. O'Brien: +353
     (0)21 864 722
    Fax +353 (0)21 378 108
    I'net Under preparation
  Open Strictly BA; telephone to arrange visit.

Traces the military development of the island of Haulbowline, from RN Dockyard & Royal Army Ordnance Corps occupation in Napoleonic times through to the present Irish Naval Service base. Paintings, photos & artefacts, mostly in restored Martello Tower.

Kilmore Quay Maritime Museum

The Lightship *Guillemot*, Kilmore Quay, Co. Wexford,
Republic of Ireland

Write The Kilmore Quay Maritime Museum, Ballyteigue,
Kilmore Quay, Co. Wexford, Republic of Ireland

Phone +353 (0)53 29655/29832

I'net http://www.elsas.demon.nl/ierland.htm

Open Daily, June–Sept, or BA

Model ships, including 5ft model of HMS *Africa*. Large collection of pictures & maritime artefacts. Displayed aboard the 1922 light vessel *Guillemot*, together with some furnishings & equipment. Local RNLI display. Audio facilities, GVs, Lib & archives BA

Limerick Museum

1 John's Square North, Limerick, Co Limerick,
Republic of Ireland

Phone +353 (0)61 417 826

I'net http://www.elsas.demon.nl/ierland.htm

Open Enquire: a move to a new location is planned

Collection of local historical artefacts includes a little maritime material: three ship models, diver's suit & pump, charts, maps & plans, photographs of vessels 1870s–1950s, bell of the vessel *Kincora*, an oar from a lifeboat of the *Lusitania*.

The Mizen Vision

Mizen Head Signal Station, near Goleen, West Cork,
Republic of Ireland

Write Mizen Tourism Co-operative Society, Harbour Road,
Goleen, or Mrs S. Hill, Heron's Cove, Goleen, West
Cork, Eire

Phone +353 (0)28 35225, 35253

Fax +353 (0)28 35422

I'net http://www.foundmark.com/Great/Westcork2.html

Open Daily, June–Sept; winter: BA

Exhibits show life of lighthouse keepers, some of the equipment, building of the Fastnet Lighthouse, sunken wrecks, marine life and collection of facsimile maps and charts.

National Maritime Museum of Ireland

Haigh Terrace, Dun Laoghaire, Co. Dublin,
Republic of Ireland

Phone +353 (0)1 280 0969

Fax +353 (0)1 284 4602

I'net http://www.dkm.ie/events/dublin/museums/
http://www.elsas.demon.nl/ierland.htm

Open Tue–Sun, May–Sept; Sun & BH in Apr & Oct; GV-BA

Artefacts illustrate Irish maritime heritage: paintings, photos, ship models (including *Sirius*), flags & charts. French 1790s longboat. Optic from Bailey lighthouse, memorabilia of *U19*, Irish shipping, naval Service & RNLI material. In ex-mariner's church. Lib Edu BA

The Queenstown Story

Cobh Heritage Centre, Cobh, Co. Cork, Republic of Ireland

Write Cobh Heritage Trust Limited, Cobh Heritage Centre, Cobh, Co. Cork, Republic of Ireland

Phone +353 (0)21 813 591

Fax +353 (0)21 813 595

I'net e-mail: cobhher@indigo.ie
http://www.cork-guide.ie/cobh/heritage-centre/index.htm

Open Daily

Multimedia exhibition on Cobh, the harbour for Cork. Emphasis on emigration, emigrant & convict ships, Cunard liners, sinking of the *Titanic* & *Lusitania*. Shipping memorabilia, maritime artefacts New genealogical information centre. AV, Edu, GV. ARC, DB BA

The Skellig Experience Heritage Centre

Valentia Island, Ring of Kerry, Co. Kerry, Republic of Ireland
(access by road bridge or ferry service)

Phone +353 (0)66 76306

Fax +353 (0)64 34506

I'net e-mail: cobhher@indigo.ie

Open Daily

Exciting multimedia exhibition telling the story of the Skellig Islands, renowned for their scenery, sea & bird life, & 161 years of lighthouse service to mariners. Lighthouse memorabilia, ship-to-shore communications, maritime artefacts. AV, MM, GV

Waterways Visitor Centre

Grand Canal Quay, Dublin 2, Republic of Ireland

Phone +353 (0)1 677 7510

Fax +353 (0)1 677 7514

I'net http://www.dkm.ie/events/dublin/museums/

Open Daily, Jun–Sept; Wed–Sun, pm only, in winter.

The story of Ireland's inland waterways, with working models and interactive multimedia presentation. AV show, IMM. On the Grand Canal Basin at Pearse Street Bridge. GV

MUSEUM SHIPS & HISTORIC VESSELS

181; OD-class hydroplane; 1980s
    National Motor Boat Museum, Basildon

Activity; east coast fishing smack; 1904
    True's Yard Fishing Heritage Centre, King's Lynn

Alarm; 14ft class racing dinghy; 1929
    ISCA Maritime Museum, Oulton Broad

Albion; Norfolk gaff-rig sailing wherry; 1898 NMV
    c/o Norfolk Wherry Trust, 14 Mount Pleasant,
    Norwich NR2 2DG

Aleida; canal tug; 1930
    The Boat Museum, Ellesmere Port

Alexandra; canal maintenance; 1882
    The Boat Museum, Ellesmere Port

Amaryllis; canal pleasure boat; 1954
    The Boat Museum, Ellesmere Port

Amy Howson (14085) ex-*Sophia*; steel-hull Humber sloop;
    1914 NMV
    Humber Keel & Sloop Preservation Soc Ltd.,
    Tel: +44 (0)1652 635288

Anglia Pipedream; multihulled proa
    ISCA Maritime Museum, Oulton Broad

Ann; rowing & sailing dingy mould; 1985
    Merseyside Maritime Museum

Anne; clinker-built, double-ended fishing 'scaffie'
    ISCA Maritime Museum, Oulton Broad

Annie; Port Isaac lugger
    ISCA Maritime Museum, Oulton Broad

Anser; duck punt
    Windermere Steamboat Museum

Antares; wooden-hulled 55ft trawler; 1965
    Scottish Maritime Museum, Irvine

Apache; offshore powerboat
    National Motor Boat Museum, Basildon

Aquila; Star class sailing dingy; 1922
    Merseyside Maritime Museum

Argo; repro of 55ft Greek galley
    ISCA Maritime Museum, Oulton Broad

Argonaut; Hastings beach punt fishing boat; 1976
    ISCA Maritime Museum, Oulton Broad

Aries; canal narrowboat; 1935
    The Boat Museum, Ellesmere Port

Arthur of Chester; river Dee salmon boat; 1979
    Merseyside Maritime Museum

Aspull; wooden ice-breaker canal boat; c1900
    The Boat Museum, Ellesmere Port

ASR-10; WW2 air-sea rescue barge; c1941
    Scottish Maritime Museum, Irvine

Atlanta 1; Flying Fifteen class yacht
    ISCA Maritime Museum, Oulton Broad

Austin Healey sports boat; 1958
    Classic Boat Museum, Newport, Isle of Wight

Autumn Mist; Flying Fifteen class yacht
    ISCA Maritime Museum, Oulton Broad

Avanti; Fenn & Wood Sportsman
    National Motor Boat Museum, Basildon

Avenger; Uffa-King class sailing dinghy
    Classic Boat Museum, Newport, Isle of Wight

Bacup; steel barge; 1950 (?)
    The Boat Museum, Ellesmere Port

Balmoral; ts diesel ferry/excursion ship; 1949 NMV
    Waverley Excursions Ltd, Anderston Quay,
    Glasgow G3 8HA

Banshee; whammel boat; c1890
    The Dock Museum, Barrow-in-Furness

Bantam II; canal tug; 1956
    The Boat Museum, Ellesmere Port

Barnabas; dipping lug St Ives mackerel driver; 1881
    Cornish Maritime Trust, Tel: +44 (0) 1726 832 224).
    Based at Falmouth

Basileus; Kneeler hydroplane; 1929
    National Motor Boat Museum, Basildon

Bass Conqueror; ocean rower
    ISCA Maritime Museum, Oulton Broad

Basuto; Clyde puffer; 1902
    The Boat Museum, Ellesmere Port

Bat Boat II; speedboat; 1912
    Southampton Maritime Museum

Bat; steam launch; 1891
    Windermere Steamboat Museum

Bedford; double-ended pulling lifeboat; 1886
    ISCA Maritime Museum, Oulton Broad

Beeston; canal tug; 1946
    The Boat Museum, Ellesmere Port

Bertha; Brunel's drag-boat; 1844
    ISCA Maritime Museum, Oulton Broad

Bertilda; Inshore fishing vessel
    East Kent Maritime Museum, Ramsgate

Bigmere; steel barge; 1948
    The Boat Museum, Ellesmere Port

Birchills; canal tug; 1957
    The Boat Museum, Ellesmere Port

Birdie; steam launch; 1899
    Merseyside Maritime Museum

Bishop's Move; Fireball racing dinghy, 16ft 10in
    ISCA Maritime Museum, Oulton Broad

Black Bess (CS32); Itchen ferry gaff rig fishing smack; 1870
    Classic Boat Museum, Newport, Isle of Wight

Black Pig; Type K Montagu whaler
    Merseyside Maritime Museum

Black Swan; Welsh coracle
    Merseyside Maritime Museum

Blossom; NE coast fishing mule (hybrid coble); 1887
Tyne & Wear Museums Service,
c/o Newcastle Discovery; in store

Blue Gannet; stepped hydroplane; 1927
National Motor Boat Museum, Basildon

Bond; Bond water skis; 1960s
National Motor Boat Museum, Basildon

Boys Own; Northumberland fishing coble; 1933
ISCA Maritime Museum, Oulton Broad

Branksome; Windermere lake steam launch; 1896
Windermere Steamboat Museum

Bream (SU222); Itchen ferry; 1912
Southampton Maritime Museum

Britania; Kiribati proa, 37ft
ISCA Maritime Museum, Oulton Broad

Britannia II; ocean rower; 1970
ISCA Maritime Museum, Oulton Broad

Britannia; composite 68ft lighterage tug; 1893 NMV
Gravesend, awaiting restoration

Britannia; ocean rower; 1968
ISCA Maritime Museum, Oulton Broad

British Peat; Eskimo umiak, 25ft
ISCA Maritime Museum, Oulton Broad

Brocklebank; motor tug; 1964
Associate Vessel of Merseyside Maritime Museum
(afloat nearby)

Brown Willy; International 14 class; 1930s
East Kent Maritime Museum, Ramsgate

Brunette; a William Fife bermuda rig yacht; 1895
Scottish Maritime Museum, Irvine

Bullet II; Kneeler hydroplane; 1929
National Motor Boat Museum, Basildon

Buttercup (No 313); West Wight scow racing dinghy; c1953
Classic Boat Museum, Newport, Isle of Wight

Buttock Up, K780; International 14 class racing dinghy
ISCA Maritime Museum, Oulton Broad

Calshot (ex-*Red Funnel*); tug tender; 1930
Southampton Maritime Museum

Calypso; Riva Florida/Chris Craft powerboat; Italy, 1954
Classic Boat Museum, Newport, Isle of Wight

Cambria; Thames spritsail barge; 1906
Dolphin Yard Sailing Barge Museum, Sittingbourne

Camelia; Morecambe Bay skiff; c1890s
Lancaster Maritime Museum

Canfly; Bowness mahogany-hulled speedboat; 1922
Windermere Steamboat Museum

Canning; oil-burning steam-powered tug; 1954
Swansea Maritime and Industrial Museum

Capella; river Dee jigger boat; 1923
Merseyside Maritime Museum

Carola; Scottish-built steam yacht; 1898
Scottish Maritime Museum, Irvine;
available for charter.

Cathead; wooden barge
  The Boat Museum, Ellesmere Port

Catherine; International 14 class racing dinghy;
  ISCA Maritime Museum, Oulton Broad

Cedar; wooden barge; c1900
  The Boat Museum, Ellesmere Port

Centaur; canal narrowboat; c1890
  The Boat Museum, Ellesmere Port

Cervia; steam tug; 1946
  East Kent Maritime Museum, Ramsgate

Charlotte; pinnace; 1930s
  National Motor Boat Museum, Basildon

Chiltern; canal narrowboat; 1946
  The Boat Museum, Ellesmere Port

Circus Girl; Bembridge Redwing; c1900
  Classic Boat Museum, Newport, Isle of Wight

City of Leicester; RNLI Boarding boat; in use until 1970s
  Walton Maritime Museum

Clover; International 14 class racing dinghy
  ISCA Maritime Museum, Oulton Broad

CMB 103; post WW1 coastal motor boat
  (MTB/Minelayer); 1921
  The Historic Dockyard, Chatham
  (on loan from IWM.)

Coconut; Grenadine (W.I.) fishing sloop
  Classic Boat Museum, Newport, Isle of Wight

Comrade ex *Ada Carter* ex *Wanda*; steel Humber Keel; 1923
  NMV
  Humber Keel & Sloop Preservation Soc Ltd.,
  Tel: +44 (0)1652 635 288

Cookie; hydroplane racing boat; 1962
  Windermere Steamboat Museum

Coronation Rose; beach pleasure boat; 1911
  Lancaster Maritime Museum

Coronation; Yarmouth shrimp boat; 1926 (view BA only)
  Maritime Museum for East Anglia, Great Yarmouth

Cosworth; Formula 1-OZ; 1970s
  National Motor Boat Museum, Basildon

Cuddington; steel boat; 1948
  The Boat Museum, Ellesmere Port

Cutty Sark; composite three-masted clipper ship; 1869
  Clipper Ship *Cutty Sark*, Greenwich (Maritime Trust)

Cygnet; swan-prowed row-boat; 1881
  ISCA Maritime Museum, Oulton Broad

Cygnet; Thornycroft steamer; 1873
  National Motor Boat Museum, Basildon

Daddy Long Legs, K334; International 14 class racing dinghy
  ISCA Maritime Museum, Oulton Broad

Daniel Adamson; iron towing boat; 1903
  The Boat Museum, Ellesmere Port

Dawn; Windermere 17ft class bermuda rig yacht; 1934
  Windermere Steamboat Museum

Daystar (ex-*Edith Nora*) LR17
    Morecambe Bay shrimper 'Nobby'; 1894
    Merseyside Maritime Museum

De Wadden; three-masted aux schooner; Netherlands, 1917
    Merseyside Maritime Museum

Defender II; powered raceboat; 1908
    National Motor Boat Museum, Basildon

Diana; Brooke launch; 1909
    National Motor Boat Museum, Basildon

Discovery, RRS; wooden barque for polar exploration; 1901
    Discovery Point, Dundee

Dolly; Lake Windermere steam launch; c1850
    Windermere Steamboat Museum

Donola; steam yacht; 1893
    National Maritime Museum, Greenwich

Dorset Lass; Beer crabber, 22ft
    ISCA Maritime Museum, Oulton Broad

Eden; motor barge
    Waterways Adventure Centre & Museum, Goole

Edmund Gardner; Liverpool pilot cutter; 1953
    Merseyside Maritime Museum (in adjacent dry dock)

Eliza; Azores double-ended whaleboat
    ISCA Maritime Museum, Oulton Broad

Elizabeth; clinker dinghy
    ISCA Maritime Museum, Oulton Broad

Elizabeth; Mersey motor gig boat; 1940
    Merseyside Maritime Museum

Ellen; Cornish, Gorran Haven crabber; 1882
    Cornish Maritime Trust, Tel: +44 (0) 1726 832 224.
    Based at Falmouth

Elsie; Morecambe Bay prawner, 27ft
    ISCA Maritime Museum, Oulton Broad

Elswick No.2; Tyne wherry; 1930s
    Tyne & Wear Museums Service, c/o Newcastle
    Discovery; in store

Elton; canal boat
    Wooden Canal Boat Society

Emily Barratt; wooden topsail schooner; 1914
    The Dock Museum, Barrow-in-Furness

Encore, K874; International 14 class racing dinghy
    ISCA Maritime Museum, Oulton Broad

Endeavour; clinker-built coxed river four; c1962
    Classic Boat Museum, Newport, Isle of Wight

Enterprise; lute-stern, clinker-built sailing lugger; 1909
    Fishermen's Museum, Hastings

Esperance; TS steam launch; 1869
    Windermere Steamboat Museum

Esther; fishing smack; 19th century
    National Fishing Heritage Centre, Grimsby

Ethel; Mersey motor gig boat/pilot boarding punt; c1937
    Merseyside Maritime Museum

Excelsior LT472; Lowestoft sailing trawler; 1921 NMV
Excelsior Sailing Trust, Lowestoft.
Tel/Fax: +44 (0) 1502 585 302

Falcon; steam launch, 1895. Kingdon steam engine
The Museum of the Broads

Far Haaf; replica sixareen
Unst Boat Haven, Haroldswick.

Faroe Boat; Bondabaturin or farmer's boat; 1903
Unst Boat Haven, Haroldswick.

Finnagain; ocean rower
ISCA Maritime Museum, Oulton Broad

Fiona 108J; Jersey carvel-built fishing boat; 1860s
The Jersey Museum, Channel Islands

Firefly K233; 14ft racing dingy; 1910
Merseyside Maritime Museum

Flamboyant Temptress; Merlin Rocket
ISCA Maritime Museum, Oulton Broad

Flying Buzzard; Clyde Shipping Co.
oil-fired steam tug; c1951
Maryport Steamboats Museum

Flying Saucer; jolly boat
ISCA Maritime Museum, Oulton Broad

Flying Spray; Thames cruising launch (petrol); 1910
Classic Boat Museum, Newport, Isle of Wight

Foam; Shetland croft boat; 1905
Unst Boat Haven, Haroldswick.

Forget me Not; wooden narrow boat
Wooden Canal Boat Society

Freda & Norah; fishing smack; early 20th century
National Fishing Heritage Centre, Grimsby

Friendship; canal narrowboat; 1925
The Boat Museum, Ellesmere Port

Gaiety 1887 (ex-*Oxford*); TS river launch; 1887 NMV
French Bros Ltd, Clewer Court Road,
Windsor SL4 5JH

Gardie Boat; whillie or eela inshore fishing boat; 1882
Unst Boat Haven, Haroldswick.

Garlandstone; River Tamar ketch; 1908/9
Morwellham Quay Open Air Museum

Garnock; Irvine Harbour Co. tugboat; 1956
Scottish Maritime Museum, Irvine

George; wooden barge; 1910
The Boat Museum, Ellesmere Port

Gifford; canal narrowboat; 1926
The Boat Museum, Ellesmere Port

Gipsy/No.1; racing dinghy, 12ft
ISCA Maritime Museum, Oulton Broad

Glenlee; Clyde-built three-masted steel barque; 1896
at Yorkhill Quay, Glasgow, for restoration.
Tel: +44 (0)141 339 0631

Glenway; Thames sailing barge
Dolphin Yard Sailing Barge Museum, Sittingbourne

Grace Darling; modern copy of her pulling coble
Trinity Maritime Centre, Newcastle-upon-Tyne

Grace Darling; pulling coble; pre-1830?
Grace Darling Museum, Bamburgh, Northumberland

Great Britain, ss; Brunel's iron screw-ship; 1843
Great Britain, Bristol

'The Green Boat'; pulling & sailing boat; 18th century
Merseyside Maritime Museum

Greyhound; coastal fishing boat; pre-1914
Unst Boat Haven, Haroldswick.

Guillemot; Lightship; 1922;
Kilmore Quay Maritime Museum

Gypsy Moth IV; Chichester's circumnavigation
of globe yacht; 1966
King William Walk, Greenwich, London.
(owner: The Maritime Trust)

H.E.; Hal Kelly hydroplane; 1950s
National Motor Boat Museum, Basildon

Hannah; River Lune whammel boat; c1910
Lancaster Maritime Museum

Harriet; fishing smack; 1893 (planned acquisition)
Fleetwood Museum

Hawk, K364; International 14 class racing dinghy
ISCA Maritime Museum, Oulton Broad

Hazel; canal boat
Wooden Canal Boat Society

Helwick, L.V.91; light vessel; 1937
Swansea Maritime and Industrial Museum

Herbert Leigh; Watson class Lifeboat; 1950
The Dock Museum, Barrow-in-Furness

Hipparcus; Hilbre Class yacht; 1966
Merseyside Maritime Museum

Hippocampus; Merlin Rocket
ISCA Maritime Museum, Oulton Broad

HMS Alliance; A-class submarine; 1947
Royal Navy Submarine Museum, Gosport

HMS Belfast; 10,500 ton *Edinburgh* Class WW2 cruiser;
1938–39
Belfast (HMS), London

HMS Bronington; minesweeper; 1953
The Bronington Trust, Wharfside, Trafford Park,
Manchester

HMS Caroline; Light cruiser, fought at Jutland; 1914 NMV
Belfast Harbour. RNR/RNVR Drill Ship, not open to
public

HMS Cavalier; Cavendish class destroyer; 1944
Hebburn, South Tyneside–but see main entry.

HMS Expunger/XE8; midget submarine; 1945
The Historic Dockyard, Chatham (on loan from IWM)

HMS Foudroyant–see HMS *Trincomalee*

HMS Gannet; composite-hulled naval sloop, sail & steam 1878
    The Historic Dockyard, Chatham. Under restoration

HMS Ocelot; *Oberon* class submarine; 1964
    The Historic Dockyard, Chatham

HMS Onyx; *Oberon* class submarine; 1966
    Historic Warships at Birkenhead

HMS Plymouth; *Rothesay* class frigate; 1959
    Historic Warships at Birkenhead

HMS Stickleback/X51; midget submarine; 1954
    Duxford Airfield (IWM), Cambridgeshire

HMS Trincomalee (one-time *Foudroyant*)
    38/26 gun Frigate; 1817
    Hartlepool Historic Quay

HMS Unicorn; 5th Rate Frigate; 1824
    The Frigate *Unicorn*, Dundee

HMS Victory; Nelson's 1st Rate 100-gun flagship; 1765
    Victory (HMS), H.M. Naval Base, Portsmouth

HMS Warrior; iron-hulled armoured steam frigate; 1860
    Warrior (HMS), H.M. Naval Base, Portsmouth,

Holland I; earliest RN submarine; 1901–05
    Royal Navy Submarine Museum, Gosport
    (under conservation)

Holm boat; Shetland & Skerries working boat; 1885
    Unst Boat Haven, Haroldswick

Hoverhawk; MK2 Hover-Air (used on White Nile Expedition); 1969
    Classic Boat Museum, Newport, Isle of Wight

HSL(S) 386; Harbour Service Launch; 1944; under restoration
    The Historic Dockyard, Chatham (on loan from IWM)

HSL102; High Speed Launch (RAF rescue boat); 1936
    Powerboat Restorations. Tel: +44 (0) 1590-624445.
    Appears at events.

Hulu; ocean rower, 30ft
    ISCA Maritime Museum, Oulton Broad

Ibis; 20ft trans-Africa exploration boat
    ISCA Maritime Museum, Oulton Broad

In Finnegan's Wake; transatlantic rower
    ISCA Maritime Museum, Oulton Broad

Irene; gaff-rig, 117ft west-country ketch; 1907 NMV
    c/o Bishops Lodge, Oakley Green, Windsor SL4 5UL: charter or BA

Ironsides; spritsail Thames sailing barge; 1900 NMV
    St Katharine's Yacht Haven, London. For charter:
    +44 (0) 1273 890 328

Iverna; Medway fishing vessel; 1893
    The Historic Dockyard, Chatham

Jacinta (FD159); Marr stern trawler; 1972
    Fleetwood fish docks. Guided tours daily.
    Phone +44 (0) 1253 824 368

James & John Young; Sailing Lifeboat
    ISCA Maritime Museum, Oulton Broad

James Caird; 23ft whaler; 1914
  (Shackleton's epic Antarctic boat)
  Dulwich College, London SE21 7LD
  BA Tel: +44 (0) 181 693 3601

Jane; Chris Craft mahogany-hulled speedboat; 1938
  Windermere Steamboat Museum

Jane; Drifter's lifeboat
  Scottish Fisheries Museum, Anstruther

Jean; Shetland whillie or eela boat; 1915
  Unst Boat Haven, Haroldswick. (under repair)

Jemima Ann; saith fishing boat; 1892
  Unst Boat Haven, Haroldswick.

Jenetta, N423; National 12ft class racing dinghy
  ISCA Maritime Museum, Oulton Broad

Jessie; Stroma Yole; latter part of 19th century
  Scottish Fisheries Museum, Anstruther

Jester; Folkboat yacht
  ISCA Maritime Museum, Oulton Broad

Jetstar; Bluebird Marine jet boat
  National Motor Boat Museum, Basildon

Jim; Dysart racing yawl; 1910
  Scottish Fisheries Museum, Anstruther

Jinx, K170; International 14 class racing dinghy
  ISCA Maritime Museum, Oulton Broad

Joan Dickson, BK52; Northumbrian fishing coble; 1947
  Marine Life & Fishing Heritage Centre, Seahouses

Joan; river Dee salmon boat; 1946
  Merseyside Maritime Museum

John & Mary Meiklam of Gladswood; motor lifeboat
  Yarmouth, Tel: +44 (0) 1493 601 893. Under
  restoration.

John & Naomi Beattie, ON 562;
  pulling & sailing lifeboat; 1906
  Swansea Maritime and Industrial Museum

John H Amos; sidepaddle steam tugboat; 1931 NMV
  River Medway, nr Chatham, awaiting restoration

John King; motor tug; 1935; under restoration
  Bristol Industrial Museum & Maritime Heritage Centre

Jolie Brise; Le Havre Pilot Cutter, 56ft
  ISCA Maritime Museum, Oulton Broad

Jubilee; Montrose salmon coble; 1977
  Scottish Fisheries Museum, Anstruther

Judy; Morecambe Bay prawner; 1904
  Fleetwood Museum

Kate (LK126); Zulu fishing boat; 1910 NMV
  Lowestoft, under restoration.

Kathleen & May; topsail schooner; 1900
  Under restoration at Gloucester
  – not open to public yet.

Katie Ann (ex *Thyme*) SA53;
  sailing/diesel beam trawler; 1921
  Swansea Maritime & Industrial Museum

Katie; Scottish Zulu Skiff fishing vessel; 1938/39
 Scottish Maritime Museum, Irvine

Kerne, no. 241 (ex-*Terrier*); *Dog* class steam tug; 1913
 Merseyside area. Accessible during 'events';
 info +44 (0) 151 606 9655

Kestrel; Bembridge Redwing with Brabazon's experimental
 aerofoil sail
 Classic Boat Museum, Newport, Isle of Wight

Keying II; Hong Kong fishing junk; 1980
 ISCA Maritime Museum, Oulton Broad

Khaki; Deal hoveller type fishing boat; 1928
 East Kent Maritime Museum, Ramsgate

Kingfisher; Fairey canvas-covered folding canoe; 1951
 Classic Boat Museum, Newport, Isle of Wight

Kingswear Castle; side-paddle pleasure steamer; 1924 NMV
 Kingswear Castle, The Historic Dockyard, Chatham,
 Kent ME4 4TQ

Kittiwake; steam launch; 1898
 Windermere Steamboat Museum

Kitty; Chris Craft 95hp inland water runabout; 1930s
 Classic Boat Museum, Newport, Isle of Wight

Klondyke; HM Customs gig; 1872
 Isles of Scilly Museum Association

Kyles; steam, converted to diesel, coaster; 1872
 Scottish Maritime Museum, Irvine

La Poupee; *Opera* class sailing dingy; 1903
 Merseyside Maritime Museum

The Ladies' Gig; 4/5 oar pulling gig; c1890
 Merseyside Maritime Museum

Lady Daphne; Thames barge; 1923. NMV (privately owned)
 St. Katherine's Dock, London
 Tel: +44 (0) 171 562 9562; Hire available.

Lady Elizabeth; steam launch; 1895
 Windermere Steamboat Museum

Lady Hamilton; motor launch; 1929
 Windermere Steamboat Museum

Lady Penelope; Chris Craft Silver Arrow powerboat;
 1957/58
 Classic Boat Museum, Newport, Isle of Wight

Laret; Dee Sailing Club racing dingy; c1933
 Merseyside Maritime Museum

Laughing Water; ballasted Shetland racing boat; 1949
 Unst Boat Haven, Haroldswick.

Les Cousins; Breton Misainier, 14ft;
 ISCA Maritime Museum, Oulton Broad

Light A 395; N.E. Yawl; 1906
 Scottish Fisheries Museum, Anstruther

Lightning; 14ft class racing dinghy; 1933
 ISCA Maritime Museum, Oulton Broad

Lightvessel 14; 137ft 550 ton displacement lightship
 Cardiff, Roath Basin

Lilian; canoe dinghy, 12ft
    ISCA Maritime Museum, Oulton Broad

Lilith; canal boat
    Wooden Canal Boat Society

Lincoln Castle; paddle steamer
    National Fishing Heritage Centre, Grimsby

Little Auk; Shetlands haddock boat; 1909
    Unst Boat Haven, Haroldswick

Little Bela; stepped hydroplane motorboat; 1928
    National Motor Boat Museum, Basildon

Little Swallow; Cromer crab boat; c1960
    Cromer Museum

Lively Hope LH 32; ringer/drifter; 1934
    Scottish Fisheries Museum, Anstruther

Lively Lady; auxiliary yawl, sailed by Sir Alec Rose; 1948
    on loan to Portsmouth museums
    (owner: The Maritime Trust)

Louise; double-expansion steam launch
    Classic Boat Museum, Newport, Isle of Wight

Lydia Eva; east coast steam herring drifter; 1930
    c/o *Lydia Eva* & *Mincarlo* Trust,
    Tel: +44 (0) 1502 677 602

Lynn II; Fenn & Wood Meteor
    National Motor Boat Museum, Basildon

Lyra; Norwegian Hardanger faering; 1934
    Unst Boat Haven, Haroldswick.

M31; offshore catamaran; 1980s
    National Motor Boat Museum, Basildon

Macandi; seine-netter; 20th century
    National Fishing Heritage Centre, Grimsby

Maggie; Ness yoal; c1900
    Unst Boat Haven, Haroldswick.

Magnum Opus; 12ft sailing dinghy
    ISCA Maritime Museum, Oulton Broad

Maid of the Isles; unballasted Shetland racing boat; 1959
    Unst Boat Haven, Haroldswick.

Mallart; Enterprise class racing dinghy, 13ft 4in
    ISCA Maritime Museum, Oulton Broad

Manana; 17ft gaff-rig sailboat; c1900
    Windermere Steamboat Museum

Manchester; canal tug; 1874
    The Boat Museum, Ellesmere Port

Marbury; wooden ice-breaker canal boat; c1900
    The Boat Museum, Ellesmere Port

Marcan Sine; Scottish fishing dinghy
    ISCA Maritime Museum, Oulton Broad

Maria; lateen-rigged Broads racing yacht; 1820s
    (view BA only)
    Maritime Museum for East Anglia, Great Yarmouth

Marktime, F2542; Firefly class racing dinghy
    ISCA Maritime Museum, Oulton Broad

Marlyn; canal maintenance
The Boat Museum, Ellesmere Port

Marsden; iron ice boat
The Boat Museum, Ellesmere Port

Mary (LK464) fishing & pleasure boat; c1900
Unst Boat Haven, Haroldswick.

Mary Anne; ferry boat for goods & livestock; c1870
Windermere Steamboat Museum

Mary Joseph; wooden 'nickey' fishing boat; c1877
Ulster Folk & Transport Museum

The Mary Rose; Henry VIII's warship; c1509–1545
The Mary Rose Trust, Portsmouth

Mary; fishing & recreation; c1932
Unst Boat Haven, Haroldswick

Mayflower; steam tug; 1861
Bristol Industrial Museum & Maritime Heritage Centre

Medicinal; Osprey Class racing dinghy; c1952
Classic Boat Museum, Newport, Isle of Wight

Medway Queen; Thames Estuary excursion paddle steamer;
1924 NMV
Under renovation at Damhead Creek, River Medway.
Tel: +44 (0) 1622 670 542

Melody W13; Attacker speed-boat; c1961
Merseyside Maritime Museum

Mendip; canal narrowboat; 1948
The Boat Museum, Ellesmere Port

Merak; canal narrowboat; 1936
The Boat Museum, Ellesmere Port

Merk; Andrews slipper stern launch; 1912
National Motor Boat Museum, Basildon

Merlin; Liverpool Bay Falcon Class racing dingy; 1955
Merseyside Maritime Museum

Merope; canal narrowboat; 1936
The Boat Museum, Ellesmere Port

Mincarlo; side trawler; 1962
c/o *Lydia Eva* & *Mincarlo* Trust,
Tel: +44 (0) 1502 677 602

Mirosa; Thames spritsail barge; 1893; NMV
Iron Wharf Boatyard, Faversham, Kent; available for
day charter, Tel: +44 (0) 1795 537 122

Miss Britain III; racing hydroplane; 1933
National Motor Boat Museum, Basildon

Miss Britain IV; world record holder diesel powerboat; 1982
National Motor Boat Museum, Basildon

Miss England; racing hydroplane; 1929
National Motor Boat Museum, Basildon

Miss Windermere IV; mahogany hulled hydroplane
speedboat; 1958
Windermere Steamboat Museum

Morgan Giles; International 14ft racing dinghy
ISCA Maritime Museum, Oulton Broad

Mossdale; wooden barge; 1875–76
The Boat Museum, Ellesmere Port

MTB 102; Vosper 68 Prototype Motor Torpedo Boat; 1937 NMV
  Lowestoft Yacht Harbour. Tel: +44 (0)1603 782 068

Mustang; Dragon class racing yacht (mahogany hull); 1963
  Classic Boat Museum, Newport, Isle of Wight

Nadja (ex *Gin*); 22 sq metre racing yacht; Sweden 1950
  Merseyside Maritime Museum

Nance; Morecambe Bay prawner; 1914
  The Dock Museum, Barrow-in-Furness
  (indoors, in frame)

Nautica; ocean rower, 20ft 8in
  ISCA Maritime Museum, Oulton Broad

Nellie; zulu or yole fishing boat; c1898 NMV
  Felixstowe

Nimbus, K316; International 14 class racing dinghy
  ISCA Maritime Museum, Oulton Broad

Nimrod; kayak; c1969
  ISCA Maritime Museum, Oulton Broad

Nordica; Formula 1 catamaran; 1980s
  National Motor Boat Museum, Basildon

North Carr Lightship; light-vessel
  Anstruther. Tel: +44 (0) 1333 310 589,
  +44 (0) 1831 621 510

Nuneham; SS steam launch; c1890s? NMV
  Runnymede Boathouse, Old Windsor,
  Berkshire SL4 2SG

Oakdale; Mersey flat; 1951
  Associate Vessel of Merseyside Maritime Museum
  (afloat nearby)

Olga SA12; 56ft gaff-rig Bristol-Channel pilot cutter; 1909
  Swansea Maritime & Industrial Museum

Osprey; teak hulled steam launch; 1902
  Windermere Steamboat Museum

Otto; steel hulled steam launch, triple expansion engine; 1896
  Windermere Steamboat Museum

Parr; sailing dinghy, 9ft
  ISCA Maritime Museum, Oulton Broad

Peggy; clinker-built schooner yacht; c1789
  The Nautical Museum, Castletown, I o M

Peggy; Sunderland foyman's coble; 1890
  Tyne & Wear Museums Service,
  c/o Newcastle Discovery; in store

Pelican; canal maintenance crane; 1956
  The Boat Museum, Ellesmere Port

Penelope II; motor launch; 1930
  Windermere Steamboat Museum

Perseverance; canal dredger; 1934
  The Boat Museum, Ellesmere Port

Petrel; eela boat; c1960
  Unst Boat Haven, Haroldswick

Phoebe; canal narrowboat
  The Boat Museum, Ellesmere Port

Phoenix; sailing dinghy, 12ft
    ISCA Maritime Museum, Oulton Broad

Pinafore; sailing dingy; c1937
    Merseyside Maritime Museum

Pinnace 1262; general-service RAF pinnace; 1942
    Scottish Maritime Museum, Irvine

Portwey; ts steam tug; 1927
    Portwey Steam Tug, North Quay, West India Dock,
    London E14

President, ex HMS *Saxifrage*; *Anchusa* class sloop; 1918 NMV
    River Thames, Victoria Embankment.
    Not open to the public.

Puffin; ocean rower; 1970
    ISCA Maritime Museum, Oulton Broad

Pyewacket; twin-engined day boat; 1960
    Windermere Steamboat Museum

Pyronaut; fire-boat; 1934
    Bristol Industrial Museum & Maritime Heritage Centre

QE3; Ocean rower, 19ft 10in
    ISCA Maritime Museum, Oulton Broad

Queen Mab; Ramsgate wherry; 1883
    East Kent Maritime Museum, Ramsgate

Queen; wooden canal boat
    Wooden Canal Boat Society

Raae; motor launch; 1938
    Windermere Steamboat Museum

Rab; Leven beach boat
    Scottish Fisheries Museum, Anstruther

Radiation; motorised wooden fishing boat; 1957
    Dundee: under renovation by local RN Aux Service
    Assoc. Not open

Ranzo (ex *Ethilda*); One-Rater class racing yacht; 1910
    Merseyside Maritime Museum

Raparee 376; Merlin-Rocket Class racing dingy; 1953
    Merseyside Maritime Museum

Raven; steam cargo vessel; 1871
    Windermere Steamboat Museum

Reaper (FR958); fifie drifter fishing boat; 1902
    Scottish Fisheries Museum, Anstruther

Reliant; Steam paddle tug; 1907
    National Maritime Museum, Greenwich

Research (LK62) (ex-*Heather Bell*);
    large Zulu fishing boat; 1903
    Anstruther harbour

Result; Kessingland beach boat
    ISCA Maritime Museum, Oulton Broad

Result; steel schooner; 1893
    Ulster Folk & Transport Museum

The Rifle; remains of a small iron steamer; c1861
    Scottish Maritime Museum, Irvine

Ripple; Shetland working, fishing & racing boat; 1928
    Unst Boat Haven, Haroldswick

Robin, ex-*Maria*; steel-hulled steam coaster 366GRT; 1890
A Maritime Trust vessel;
not normally open to the public

Rooster; Ventnor hydroplane; 1950s
National Motor Boat Museum, Basildon

Ross Tiger; sidewinder trawler; 1950s
National Fishing Heritage Centre, Grimsby

Ruby; Salmon boat, 20ft
ISCA Maritime Museum, Oulton Broad

Sabrina; clinker rowing boat
ISCA Maritime Museum, Oulton Broad

Sandfast; Simmonds motorboat; 1960s
National Motor Boat Museum, Basildon

Sapphire; Thames river launch; 1908 NMV
c/o Bishops Lodge, Oakley Green, Windsor SL4 5UL:
charter or BA

Sarah Abbott; steel barge; 1948
The Boat Museum, Ellesmere Port

Saskia II, F2324; *Firefly* class racing dinghy
ISCA Maritime Museum, Oulton Broad

Scorpio; wooden barge; c1890
The Boat Museum, Ellesmere Port

Sea Raven; Hillyard?
ISCA Maritime Museum, Oulton Broad

Seamew; motor launch, clinker built; c1908
Scottish Maritime Museum, Irvine

Seamew; sailing coble; c1900
Kirkleatham Old Hall Museum, Redcar

Seiont II; steam dredger; 1937
Seiont II Maritime Museum, Caernarfon

Shad; canal narrowboat; 1936
The Boat Museum, Ellesmere Port

Shamrock; 45ft Colchester oyster smack
ISCA Maritime Museum, Oulton Broad

Shamrock; wooden Tamar sailing barge; 1899
Cotehele Quay Museum, Saltash

Shieldhall; steamship; 1955 NMV
Southampton. Available for local cruises,
charter Tel: +44 (0) 1703 225 853

Shun Lee; Hong Kong sampan; 1973
ISCA Maritime Museum, Oulton Broad

Sir James Knott; Oakley class lifeboat; 19th century
Kirkleatham Old Hall Museum

Sir Walter Scott; triple-expansion, screw steamer; 1899 NMV
Trossachs Pier, Loch Katrine.
Bookings & Info: +44 (0) 1877 376 316

Sir William Priestley; Morecambe fishermen's lifeboat; 1934
Lancaster Maritime Museum

Snow Fly; *Firefly* Class 2-man racing dinghy
Classic Boat Museum, Newport, Isle of Wight

Sobriety; motor barge based on Humber keel
Waterways Adventure Centre & Museum, Goole

Softwing; gaff-rig Truro river oyster dredger; 1900
  Cornish Maritime Trust Tel: +44 (0) 1726 832 224.
  Based at Falmouth

Solitaire; rowing skiff; 1908
  ISCA Maritime Museum, Oulton Broad

Sonia; Dowty turbo craft
  National Motor Boat Museum, Basildon

Sorcerer, K551; International 14 class racing dinghy
  ISCA Maritime Museum, Oulton Broad

Sotero; River Tagus gaff-rig lighter; c1950
  ISCA Maritime Museum, Oulton Broad

Southam; canal boat, with BMC engine
  Wooden Canal Boat Society

Southsea; ex Isle of Wight ferry; 1948 NMV
  Southampton, undergoing restoration

Spartan; ex-Admiralty victualling inshore craft, #18; 1942
  Scottish Maritime Museum, Irvine

Speedwell; wooden barge; 1925
  The Boat Museum, Ellesmere Port

Spindrift; West Cheshire Clipper class sailing dingy; 1950
  Merseyside Maritime Museum

Spry; Severn trow
  Due to form part of Ironbridge Museum, at Coalport.
  Not yet open.

Spurn Light Vessel; 1927
  Spurn lightship, Hull Marina

St. Cybi; self-righting 52ft Barnett Class lifeboat; 1950
  Scottish Maritime Museum, Irvine

St. Just; Margate One Design dinghy; 1930s
  East Kent Maritime Museum, Ramsgate

Strandby; fishing trawler; 1941 (Danish-built)
  East Kent Maritime Museum, Ramsgate

Stratford; iron ice-breaker canal boat
  The Boat Museum, Ellesmere Port

Sue, K215; International 14 class racing dinghy
  ISCA Maritime Museum, Oulton Broad

Sunbeam; cutter yacht; c1925
  Merseyside Maritime Museum

Sundowner; Admiralty launch, used at Dunkirk; 1912
  East Kent Maritime Museum, Ramsgate

Sunny South; gaff cutter fishing boat; 1904
  ISCA Maritime Museum, Oulton Broad

Sunshine; Picarooner, 18ft
  ISCA Maritime Museum, Oulton Broad

Surfury; offshore powerboat; 1965
  National Motor Boat Museum, Basildon

Swallow; teak hulled steam launch; 1911
  Windermere Steamboat Museum

Swallow; zulu yawl or skiff; 1920–40s?
  Scottish Fisheries Museum, Anstruther

Swan; Scottish fifie herring lugger; 1900
  The Swan Trust, 18 Alexandra Buildings, Lerwick,
  Shetland

Swift; zulu yawl; 1909–1911?
> Scottish Fisheries Museum, Anstruther

T.G.B.; Watson class 47ft lifeboat; 1962
> Scottish Maritime Museum, Irvine

Tammynorie; Northern Isles yawl; 1992
> Scottish Fisheries Museum, Anstruther

Tarka; pram dinghy, 9ft 2in
> ISCA Maritime Museum, Oulton Broad

Tattershall Castle; Humber ferry paddle steamer; 1934 NMV
> King's Reach, Victoria Embankment,
> London SW1A 2HR

Thames Launch; Thames launch; 1920s
> National Motor Boat Museum, Basildon

Thomas Kirk Wright; ex-Poole lifeboat; 1938–62
> Old Lifeboat House, East Quay Road,
> or ask RNLI HQ, Poole.

Three Brothers Grant (HL154); sailing coble; 1921
> Museum of Hartlepool

Three Brothers; sailing coble; 1912
> Bridlington, (c/o Harbour Office),
> Humberside YO15 2NR

Thunderbolt; aluminium water-ski boat; 1960s
> National Motor Boat Museum, Basildon

Thyme, K523; International 14 class racing dinghy
> ISCA Maritime Museum, Oulton Broad

Tiaryara, K396; International 14 class racing dinghy
> ISCA Maritime Museum, Oulton Broad

Tiddler; German 1930s design folding canoe
> Classic Boat Museum, Newport, Isle of Wight

Tiger; clinker-built yacht-tender dinghy; 1950s
> Classic Boat Museum, Newport, Isle of Wight

Titmouse; teak-hulled gaff rig yacht; Bombay, 1890–95?
> Classic Boat Museum, Newport, Isle of Wight

Trent; canoe, 15ft
> ISCA Maritime Museum, Oulton Broad

Trident; offshore powerboat; 1950s
> National Motor Boat Museum, Basildon

Trilby; Mylne Class, Bermudian sloop racing yacht; 1936
> Merseyside Maritime Museum

Turbinia; C A Parsons' experimental steam turbine launch;
> 1894
> Newcastle Discovery

Tyne/Calshot Spirit; lightship; 1880s
> Royal Northumberland Yacht Club; Blyth

U-534; German WW2 submarine; sunk 5 May 1945,
> recently raised
> Historic Warships at Birkenhead

U475; 'Foxtrot' class submarine; USSR c1967
> Russian Submarine, Folkestone Harbour, Kent

Ulysses, K884; International 14 class racing dinghy
> ISCA Maritime Museum, Oulton Broad

Uncle Sam; clinker-built 'Dispro' motor boat; 1924
Windermere Steamboat Museum

unnamed; Broads traditional 3/4 load reed lighter; 1890
The Museum of the Broads

unnamed; Gt Yarmouth & Waveney Commissioners diesel
launch; 1935
The Museum of the Broads

unnamed; Orkney yole; 1930s
Scottish Fisheries Museum, Anstruther

unnamed; Thornycroft seaplane lighter; 1917/18
Fleet Air Arm Museum, Yeovilton

Vagrant; late Victorian small racing yacht; 1884
Scottish Maritime Museum, Irvine

Vanessa; Cornish fishing lugger; 1899
National Fishing Heritage Centre, Grimsby

Vectar 351; small jet boat prototype; 1980s
National Motor Boat Museum, Basildon

Ventnor; 3-point hydroplane; 1938
National Motor Boat Museum, Basildon

VIC32; ex-RN victualling craft; 1943. NMV
For hire, not a museum ship
Highland Steamboat Holidays, Lochgilphead.
Tel: +44 (0) 1546 510 232 to book

VIC56; ex-RN victualling inshore craft; 1945. NMV
Privately owned, she appears at maritime events
Tel:+44 (0) 181 670 9247

VIC96; ex-RN victualling steam lighter; 1954
Maryport Steamships Museum

Vigilant; 22 sq ft class
ISCA Maritime Museum, Oulton Broad

Virago; racing dinghy, 22ft 3in
ISCA Maritime Museum, Oulton Broad

Volente; double-ended fishing boat; c1948
Kirkleatham Old Hall Museum, Redcar

Wappenshall; iron ice boat
The Boat Museum, Ellesmere Port

Wasp; Riva Ariston
National Motor Boat Museum, Basildon

Water Viper; steam launch; 1907
Windermere Steamboat Museum

Waterlily; steam launch; 1866
National Maritime Museum, Greenwich

Watkin Williams; Watson class lifeboat
Welsh Industrial & Maritime Museum

Waverley; side-paddle steamer; 1947 NMV
Waverley Excursions Ltd, Anderston Quay,
Glasgow G3 8HA

Wayfarer; Chris Craft cabin cruiser; 1935
Windermere Steamboat Museum

Wheldale; 'Tom Pudding' Aire & Calder coal tug
Waterways Adventure Centre & Museum, Goole

White Lady II; racing hydroplane; 1930s
National Motor Boat Museum, Basildon

White Rose; gaff cutter yacht; 1897
The Dock Museum, Barrow-in-Furness

White Wing ME 113; baldie; 1917
Scottish Fisheries Museum, Anstruther

Whydah; three-man canoe, 18ft
ISCA Maritime Museum, Oulton Broad

Wicked Lady (ex-*Ideal*); yacht; 1889
Southampton Maritime Museum

Wild Fowl; gun punt; 1930s
National Motor Boat Museum, Basildon

Willdora; zulu type fishing boat; 1901
St Peter's Basin, River Tyne

William Gammon; Watson-class lifeboat; 1947
Swansea Maritime & Industrial Museum

Wincham; river Weaver packet; 1948
Associate Vessel of Merseyside Maritime Museum
(afloat nearby)

Wind Whistler, K952; International 14 class racing dinghy
ISCA Maritime Museum, Oulton Broad

Wingfield Castle; paddle steamer; 1934
Museum of Hartlepool

Worcester; canal tug; 1908
The Boat Museum, Ellesmere Port

Wun Betta; ocean sculler, 6ft 6in
ISCA Maritime Museum, Oulton Broad

Xavega; 52ft Portuguese Barco do Mar
ISCA Maritime Museum, Oulton Broad

Yazoo; Graduate class sailing dinghy
ISCA Maritime Museum, Oulton Broad

Zelva (ex-*Julnar*, *Joan*); Edwardian 8m racing yacht; 1907
Swansea Maritime and Industrial Museum

Zetland; world's oldest surviving lifeboat; 1802
Zetland RNLI Lifeboat Museum

Zeus, K500; International 14 class racing dinghy
ISCA Maritime Museum, Oulton Broad

INDEX